TIMBER

Timber

Rik Middleton

Aidan Walker
Series Editor

ARGUS BOOKS

Argus Books Limited
Wolsey House
Wolsey Road
Hemel Hempstead
Hertfordshire HP2 4SS
England

First published by Argus Books 1989

ISBN 0 85242 955 X

Phototypesetting by Goodfellow & Egan Ltd., Cambridge
Printed and bound by LR Printing Services Ltd., Manor Royal, Crawley, West Sussex, RH10 2QN, England

CONTENTS

ACKNOWLEDGEMENTS

My thanks are due to the following for help, time and ideas freely given:

Eileen Kenning – for the acorn.
Ailstone Hardwoods.
British Wood Preservation Association.
Friends of the Earth.
Forestry Commission.
Forestry Industries Committee of Great Britain.
Hicksons Timber Products Ltd.
Kilrot.
Living Wood Training (Mike Abbott).
Malaysian Rubber Products Research Association.
Mid Warwickshire College.
Protimeter.
Rentokil.
Southern and Western USA Forest Products Association.
Timber Research and Development Association.
Timber Trades Federation.
J. O. Walker Timber Supplies.

INTRODUCTION

From ancient times, man has had to make the materials he has to hand work for him in his everyday tasks and to overcome his problems of survival. One of his earliest and most basic materials was wood, and one of his first studies must have been to determine the properties of the wood from different trees. This differentiation of timber properties and their practical application is now advanced and is the subject of sophisticated design and construction considerations. The timber properties which early man must have found so useful to his survival are themselves the result of the evolution of trees to overcome their own survival problems.

This book gives a general picture of the physical structures of timbers, concentrating on aspects which affect our structural and aesthetic use of the material, and relates them back to their origins in the biology of the tree. It is not as detailed as most texts at the microscopic level although microscopic details cannot be entirely omitted. (For fuller information see *The Structure of Wood* by F. W. Jane, revised by Wilson and White, or their own academic text – *The Anatomy of Wood*).

The book is designed to be read sequentially but there is no need to do this. There are chapters on timber pests, chemicals in wood, seasoning, and tropical forest conservation debate, which can be read in isolation. The first two chapters concentrate on the biological aspects of wood structure and the reader may prefer to 'dip back' into these for the fuller story, particularly while reading about timber conversion or the visual aspects of timber surfaces.

I have attempted to keep the text non-academic although my profession as a Biology teacher may occasionally show through. Apart from some elementary graphical analysis, I have omitted most of the mathematical considerations which are applied to aspects of seasoning and strength testing. The Timber Research and Development Association can be consulted by the reader seeking fuller details in these areas. I have included some technical details of the chemical nature of timbers. The reader may wish to gloss over some of this, but I suggest that the structural formulae in Chapter Six can be viewed as simple 'meccano' type shapes rather than shunned as complexities.

I hope that in this book I give the woodworking reader an understanding of the materials with which we work, while properly relating these to the trees which grace first our landscape and then our workshops and homes.

Throughout, the facts related are as I understand them and the views expressed are my own.

Rik Middleton,
Coventry, 1988

CHAPTER 1

TREE GROWTH

A tree grows from a seed. It must absorb water, put down roots and go upward in search of light for the energy to make food before its meagre ration runs out and it dies of starvation. The majority do die in this way, deprived of light by their parents and neighbours. The seedling, therefore, responds first to gravity to grow up, and then to light. It does this by a simple chemical guidance system. A chemical (auxin) produced at the tip is transported towards the lower or more shaded side of a growing stem and increases elongation. This causes a bending towards the light (phototropism) and away from gravity (geotropism). This system will control the actively growing parts of a tree throughout its life and will be responsible for the growth form of the tree and consequently its usefulness as timber.

When they·expand, leaves produce other control chemicals (kinins) which affect the growth of the tree, tending to slow it down and encourage the development of the different kinds of tissues required. They also control the leaf's own lifespan. This triggers another chemical (dormin) which controls the dormancy cycles and hence the growth ring structures which give so many timbers their character.

Leaves are used to catch light energy and use it to convert carbon dioxide from the air into plant material in order to grow. Leaves which cannot do this adequately because of insufficient light, age, die and are prematurely shed. The chemical growth controls transfer growth to more profitable areas, usually higher up. Branches overshadowed will be abandoned by the tree as a whole when they fail to make their quota of food and control chemicals.

The growth form of a tree is profoundly affected by surrounding shade and competitively growing neighbours. A majority of trees produce more valuable timber when grown alongside other similar trees, although this seldom happens in nature.

Most trees in Britain and across Europe shed their leaves in winter to avoid drying out when ground water freezes. It may seem unnecessary now but our trees evolved over long periods of time when this happened periodically in ice ages. In spring, buds open, leaves expand and fill with fluid. In the case of a large tree, the fluid content of the leaves may be hundreds of litres. The leaves then open pores (stomata) to absorb carbon dioxide. As they do so, their own water is carried away by evaporation.

This loss of water vapour by the leaves is called 'transpiration' and it may run into hundreds of litres a day. This places an enormous demand on the root system to replace this water and on the trunk to transport it at an adequate rate. Water and the mineral nutrients it carries are transported upward in the material we know as wood. A botanist calls this woody tissue 'xylem' (pronounced 'zylem') and recognises it in all true land plants. Herbaceous plants produce small threads of it which do not last. Woody plants – our trees and shrubs – lay down coherent blocks of this tissue and add to them each year from the outer layers.

The xylem is a beautifully adapted but mostly dead tissue. A living plant cell contains gelatinous cytoplasm around a fluid filled space (vacuole) within what is essentially a strong paper box of its own making (cellulose cell wall) (see Fig. 1).

Xylem cells are elongated parallel to the main axis of the stem. Their living cytoplasm chemically impregnates its own cellulose cell wall with the more rigid and waterproof substance – lignin.

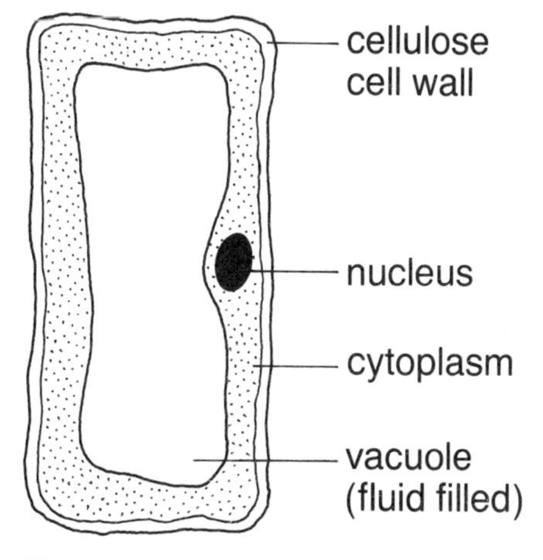

Fig. 1 *A generalised plant cell.*

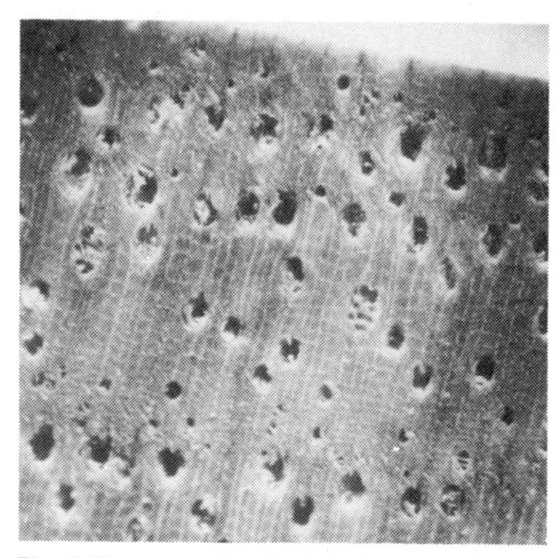

Fig. 2 *Hickory endgrain showing vessel pores.*

It does this in a variety of intricate patterns – rings, spirals and reticulate patterns with finely sculpted interconnecting holes called pits joining adjacent cells. The living contents of all but a few then commit biochemical hara-kiri and rapidly disintegrate. This leaves them hollow, liquid filled and ready to transport water. Some xylem cells are relatively wide and interconnect end to end with almost complete breakdown of endwalls. These are called vessels and are responsible for the pores easily visible in the endgrain of some timbers. These form continuous hollow tubes ideally suited to the rapid transport of water (see Fig. 3).

Most xylem cells are smaller in diameter and have pointed ends which interdigitate with others above and below instead of meeting end on. These are called tracheids (see Fig. 4). They are not open at the ends but between the lignin patterns in the cell wall is cellulose. This can look very like paper of even fabric under an electron microscope. The spaces between the fibres are large in molecular terms, so water and dissolved

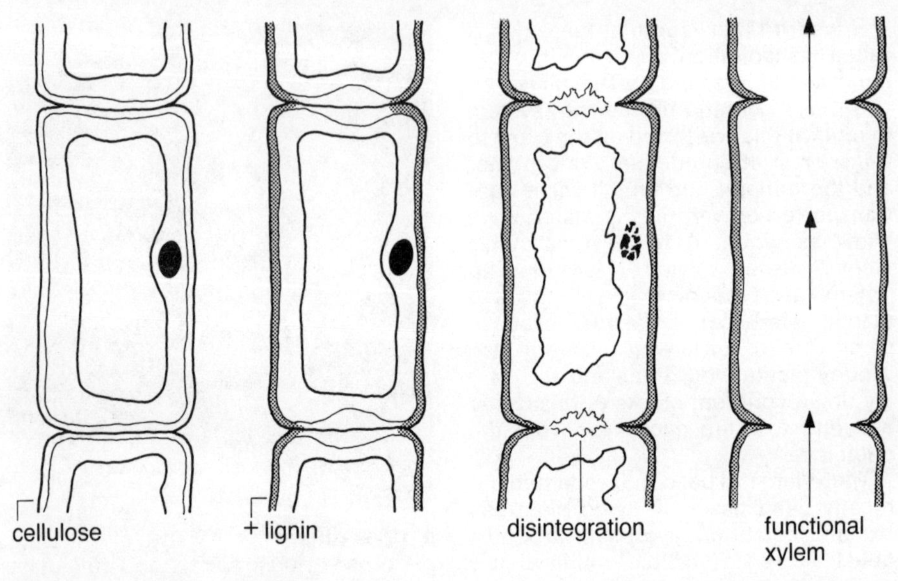

Fig. 3 *Xylem vessel development.*

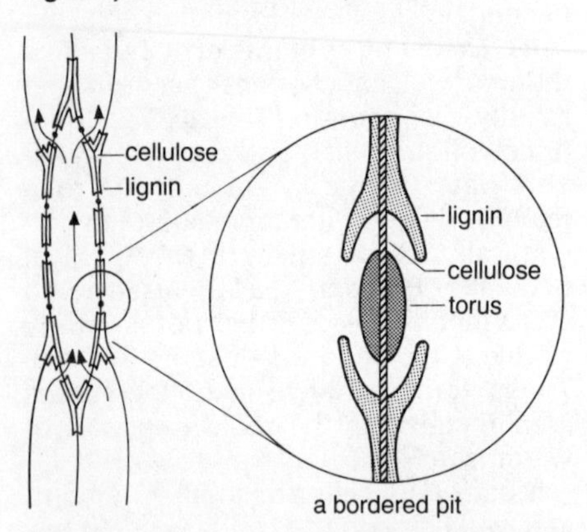

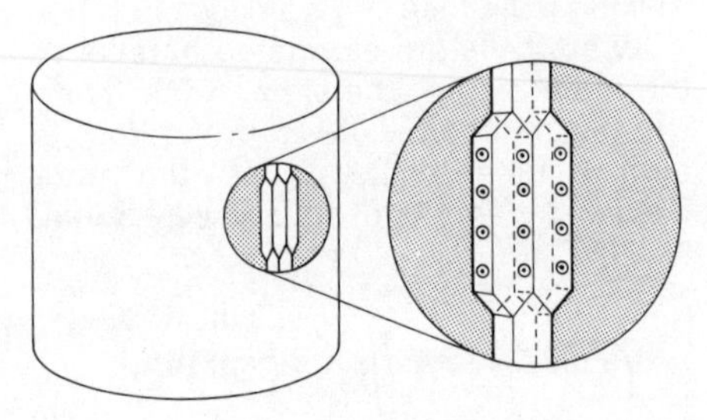

Fig. 4 *(left) Tracheids.*

Fig 5 *(above) Bordered pits on radial walls.*

substances have no difficulty in passing through from one cell space to the next. Tracheids cannot transmit water as rapidly as vessels, but they are more versatile in that they are able to transmit it sideways or at an angle upward rather than in strict lines. To facilitate this, tracheids have special sculpted holes in their radial interconnecting walls. These are called bordered pits. There is a raised border in the lignin on both sides and a central plug of lignin – the torus. Around this the cellulose layer is permeable. These allow water sideways from one tracheid to the next contemporary tracheid. It cannot pass as easily to the older ones inside nor the younger ones outside, as these pits don't usually occur on tangential walls. More cunning yet, to seal off any areas of uncontrolled water loss a pressure difference between the two cells will push the torus over and seal the hole. This becomes permanent if it remains pressed over for some time.

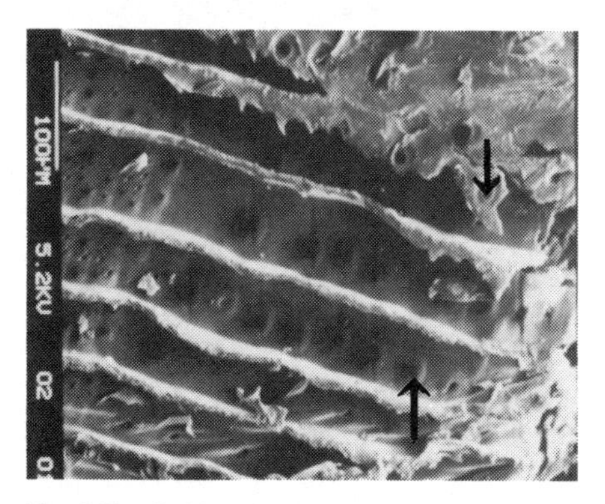

Fig. 6 *Tracheids with bordered pits (arrowed).*

Water is raised in the trunk of a tree almost entirely by being drawn up from above. Leaves transpire and withdraw water from the xylem in the twigs by capillary action. This causes a reduced pressure which draws water upward. When this pressure deficit is transmitted hydraulically to the roots it enables them to increase their demand for soil water. The living tissues in the root are essential for water uptake from soil but, from there on, it is a physical rather than a biological process. Some trees, such as birch can actually push water up by root pressure during leaf expansion, but this is not general.

So, when water is travelling up the trunk the xylem contents are under reduced pressure. This can be seen if a small vertical strip of bark is removed and a plasticine cup put up against the xylem so exposed. The cup can be filled with ink and a small puncture made below the level of the ink. Ink is almost instantly sucked both up and down into the punctured xylem.

A small proportion of xylem cells do not die when they mature but retain their living contents and form continuous networks of living cells throughout the outer xylem. This is called xylem parenchyma and it can form continuous bands in all directions through the wood. Its function is to move materials other than water and minerals around within the woody tissue and, in some cases, to store them. In winter, much of this living tissue stores the starch which provides the energy and materials to get growth off to a competitively rapid start in spring.

Parenchyma can be easily studied in small winter branches by applying tincture of iodine to cut surfaces. The yellow/orange iodine solution turns the starch a deep blue-black so location of these cells is very easy.

Parenchyma exists in continuous lines along the axis of the trunk. The distribution of these in a cross section of the wood show several distinct pattern types. These are described as bounded, banded, paratracheal or apotracheal, vasicentric or aliform and a variety of other technical terms. Study of these

Fig. 7 *Apple branch with and without iodine staining.*

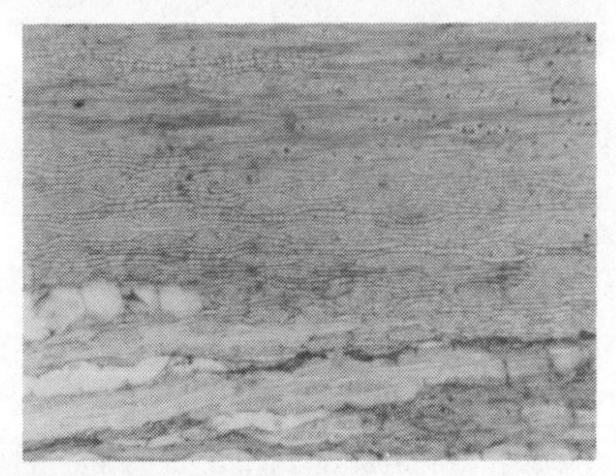

Fig. 8 *Ash – a single size of ray.*

under a microscope or powerful hand lens is essential to the proper identification of timber but is beyond the scope of this book.

Parenchyma also exists as a quite distinct radially arranged system. Rays, also called medullary rays are mostly parenchyma strands which run from the newest xylem cells to the outside of the trunk in towards the central axis. A few such strands reach all the way to the centre; most stop somewhere within the trunk. This ray system can be quite insignificant in most conifers e.g. pine, but can be very extensive in some broad-leaved trees such as oak and plane.

There can be a variety of sizes of ray. Some trees have a single size in terms of vertical height, e.g. ash, while others have two distinctly different sizes, e.g. oak. In some cases, ray sizes defy this kind of classification. This is true of hornbeam where they branch vertically into the rays above and below (aggregate rays).

Rays remain at more or less constant spacing looked at on the circumference. This means that, as the tree grows in girth, new rays have to be initiated. This occurs at the beginning of a new year's growth. Once a ray is initiated, it is

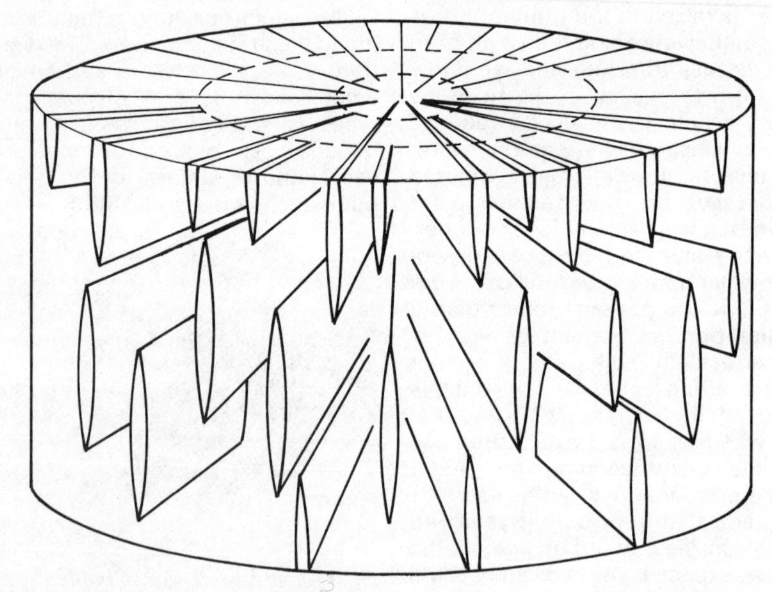

Fig. 9 *The ray system with other parts removed.*

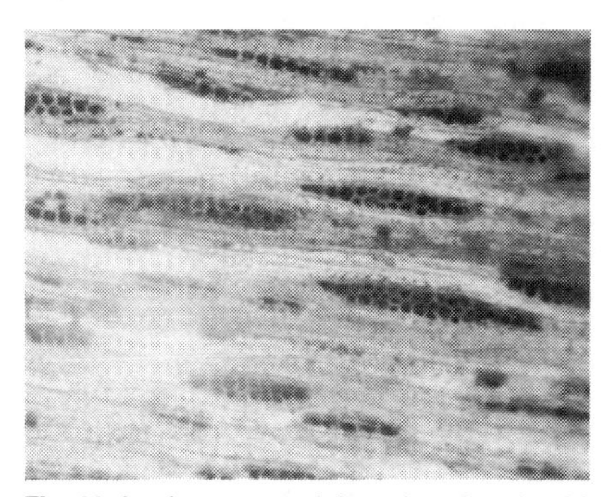

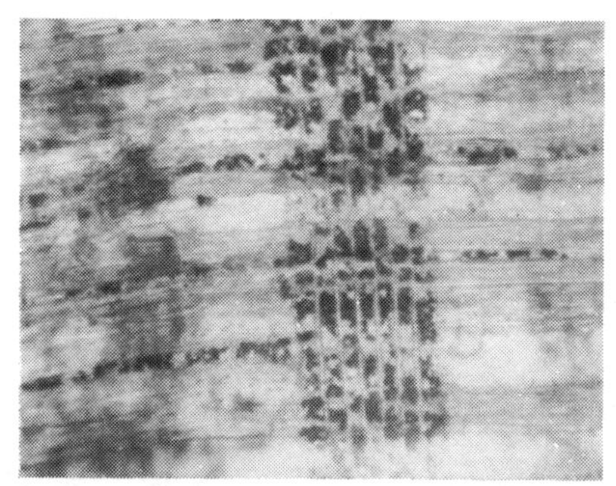

Fig. 10 *Apple – tangential section showing biseriate rays and uniseriate rays iodine stained – black spots are starch grains.* **Fig. 11** *Apple – radial section showing ray cut lengthwise.*

persistent and runs unbranched to the periphery.

Looked at from the periphery, that is tangentially, rays can be only one cell wide (uniseriate) or they may be many cells wide at the widest point (multiseriate) although they always taper off to one cell wide top and bottom. The cells within the rays may be elongated in the direction of the ray (procumbent) or in the direction of the stem axis – (upright). In many timbers, upright cells tend to occupy the top and bottom positions. In the conifers, some or all of the cells in a ray may be tracheids. In broad-leaved trees, they are always parenchyma. The radial systems are responsible for the visual effects in some of the most spectacularly figured woods (see Chapter Five). Analysis of ray structures is a fundamental part of timber recognition and identification both at the visual and microscopic levels.

Wood transports water and minerals up and other materials in and out in the radial system. It transports nothing downward. But downward transport does occur in a much less extensive tissue which forms a ring outside the wood on the inner layer of the bark. It is called phloem (pronounced 'flow- em') and, since it does not produce lignin or any other resistant materials, it does not usually persist. It consists of cells not unlike xylem tracheids in size and axial elongation. Some of these (sieve tubes) are perforated on their confluent end walls and are unusual in losing their nucleus but not their cytoplasm.

Other cells remain entire (companion cells). This tissue transports food, made in the leaves, down to the root structures. The roots are the source of the mineral food of the plant but have to have a supply of carbohydrates – the phloem feeds down a constant stream of sucrose sugar. This makes the phloem a highly nutritious tissue for animal consumption and, in some circumstances, it is extracted and eaten. Deer, squirrels and rabbits will do this in severe winters and this is the reason for the insect attacks on bark, such as those which spread Dutch elm disease. Deer stags may also damage bark wearing the felt off their new antlers. If the phloem is sufficiently damaged in this way, or by foresters 'ringing' the tree, then the root starves to death and fails to absorb water and minerals. Death of the tree is then inevitable.

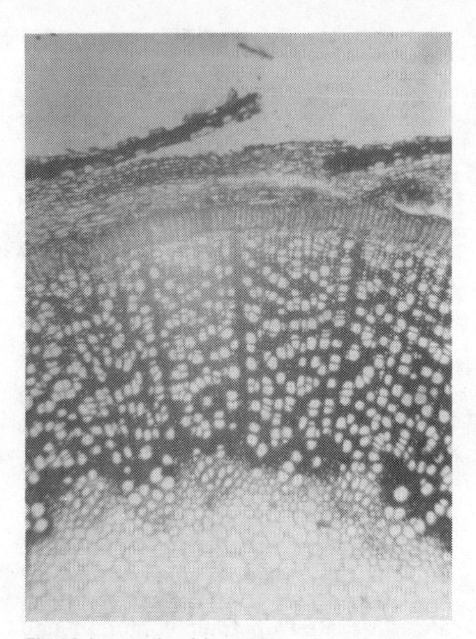

Fig 12 *Layers in elder stem.*

In order to protect the phloem, another tissue outside it, the phellogen, produces a firm waterproof mass of spongy waxy dead cells, often impregnated with bitter tasting chemicals and this is what we see as the outside of the bark. This tissue, known as phellem, is identical with cork which is the particularly thick and soft phellem layer of the Spanish cork oak. Its variety of colours and textures enables the naturalist to identify trees in winter and it protects the inner tissues against claws, teeth, antlers, boring insects and also extremes of temperature. The phellem grows constantly from the phellogen layer and may be worn away or flake off as it does in London plane.

The first threads of xylem and phloem in new growth come from the elongation of cells produced by the growing tip of the plant. As soon as elongation of the cells has finished at a given point on a growing lead shoot, xylem and phloem have to be added alongside the slender trace which supplied the needs of the growing tip.

Perhaps the most complex living tissue of the tree, and the one directly responsible for the nature of the timber, is the vascular cambium. Strangely, for such a complex and important tissue, it can be very hard to find under the microscope even though its position in the trunk is quite specific and defined. It occurs on the outer layer of the xylem and the inner layer of the phloem forming the boundary layer between the wood and the bark. It is a tissue of thin walled living cells and so is the layer at which the bark naturally parts company with the underlying wood.

Cambium is directly responsible for the production of phloem and the more extensive xylem. It is a microscopic layer but it alone produces the mass of wood in all its structural complexity. From before bud-break to near leaf-fall, cambium cells are in a state of constant activity. The cambium cell absorbs food materials from the phloem, grows and then goes through the complex process of reproducing its nucleus (mitosis). Having now two nuclei, it produces new cell wall materials between the nuclei in a plane parallel to the stem circumference i.e. tangentially. Two complete cells result. One of these will repeat this process immediately, while the other will develop into a phloem cell if it is on the outside and a xylem cell if it is to the inside. How such intense and complex activity and differentiation is achieved in a layer essentially one cell thick is one of the marvellous mysteries of biology.

Most of the cambium cells are already elongated in the axial direction so the cells it produces lie in the correct plane. Some cambium cells, however, divide up into brick shaped cells which produce new cells less frequently but allow them to elongate radially. In doing so they form the medullary ray system (see Fig. 13).

Cells produced and left to the inside of the layer of cell division activity become xylem cells. They form and differentiate by a process which may include vast sideways expansion and/or intrusive length increase to push between cells above and below. They have to produce very specifically sculpted impregnations of lignin and some other materials into their cellulose walls and then, if they are not to become part of a parenchyma strand, their cytoplasm and nucleus autolyse (digest themselves). Only then can they be considered functional xylem cells and pass into service. To add to even this awesome level of complexity, throughout the growing season the type of xylem cell produced in the axial system changes in a precisely controlled way characteristic of each tree species.

In the early part of the growth season, xylem is produced for rapid spring sap ascent. This will tend to be the larger diameter sizes of xylem element produced in that species. In haste to be pressed into service, it will probably show a minimum length increase and a minimum lignin thickness. As the season progresses the need for more water transport tissue becomes less pressing but, of course, the other function of the xylem is support of the considerable mass of the tree. Differentiation of xylem towards the end of the season concentrates more on this second function, and increasingly some cells are produced which grow intrusively between other cells at their ends, which do not enlarge much in diameter and which have

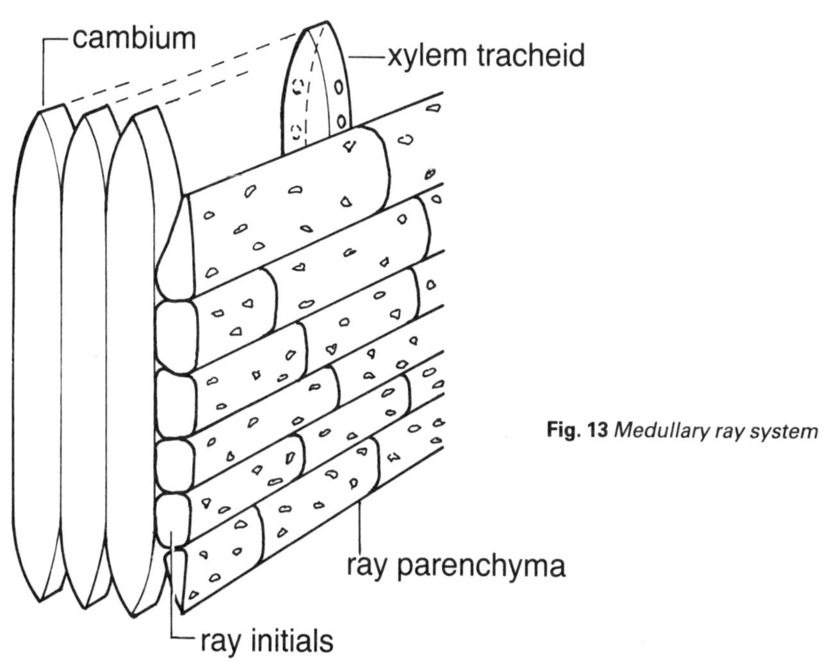

Fig. 13 *Medullary ray system*

thicker and less complex lignin strengthening. Then, around the time of leaf colouration in autumn, the cambium becomes dormant for the winter or other unfavourable season. Next spring, or whenever growth resumes, the larger, thinner walled cells will form immediately outside the more dense autumn production. This sharp demarcation line gives a more or less distinct visual break between complete rings around the tree trunk seen in cross section. This is called

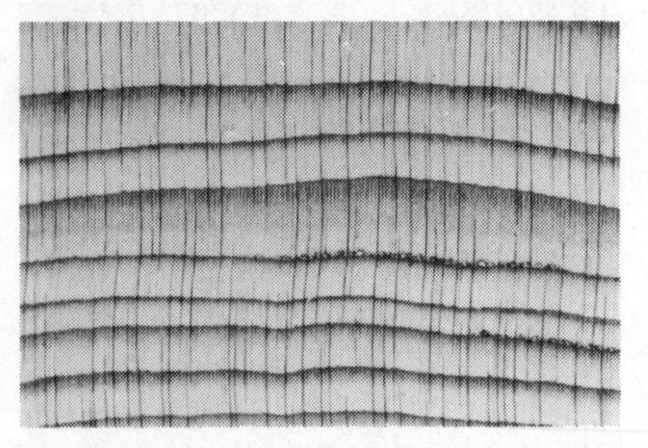

Fig. 14 *Annual rings – hemlock.*

an annual ring and it is usually true that it represents one year's growth. Autumn wood is almost always darker than spring wood. The variety and beauty of the markings that this can produce on a cut surface of timber is the subject of Chapter Five.

As the tree grows and concentrates its light and carbon dioxide gathering mechanisms higher up, lower branches may be discarded as they become overshaded. The tree has no mechanism for discarding defunct branches as it has for the active shedding of leaves. The branch which for many years grew out of the side of the trunk as an integral part of the tree will die and become subject to normal decay. While a living part of the growing trunk, the xylem of the branch was one with the trunk xylem and formed a radially organised section at an angle, characteristic of the tree species, through it. Once it is dead it is merely a foreign body which continued growth of the trunk simply envelops. Growth of the trunk xylem will occur around it but can no longer integrate with it. Any remains of bark on the branch will form a barrier which isolates the branch xylem, which may be perfectly sound timber, from the trunk xylem. Where a branch was living and integrated it produces what is called a live knot which, in cut timber, may be a weak point and/or a decorative feature. Where it was dead, it forms a dead knot which may well fall out leaving a hole lined with black bark remains. Live knots are more or less of a timber defect depending on how the timber is converted (see Chapter Three). Dead knots would always be considered a serious defect in timber in constructional terms. Fortunately, however, it is not beyond the wit of man to incorporate holes and black spots into the decorative and artistic use of wood.

Every visible feature in a piece of wood has something to say about the tree's struggle for survival and the complex and active ways in which it has evolved to cope with competition, predation and parasites.

Fig. 15 *One of next century's dead knots.*

CHAPTER 2

TYPES OF WOOD

The oldest tree-form land plants evolved a very long time ago. Dinosaurs must have browsed on them. They were much simpler than some which can be found today. However, it is in the nature of evolution that some organisms progress and change while others sometimes retrench and find a niche in the natural world which allows them to survive unchanged. The nautilus, the crocodile and tropical tree ferns, date with very little change from the early dinosaur age or before. So with the plants from which we use timber: some are of greater antiquity and relatively more simple and unspecialised, others show advance into new forms of greater complexity.

We believe that the original form of xylem cell was the tracheid. A tree with only tracheids in its xylem would have to live in a very lush, moist habitat or have limited leaf area, as tracheids transport water at only modest speed compared to the wider and more open vessel. For maximum support these tracheids would have to be quite long. The ray structure would be absent or very simple. Such primitive plants, while growing from seed, have a simpler method of producing them. They hark back to a time before flowers. The plant I am describing is not uncommon in suburban gardens; it is the monkey puzzle tree (*Araucaria*). Its timber, or rather a very close relative, is to be found in some timber suppliers lists as parana.

Fig. 16 *The monkey puzzle tree (*Araucaria *sp.).*

Its tracheids are over a centimetre in length, which is enormous by the standard of their width. Its leaves show the thick succulence with a waxy waterproof cuticle to limit its water loss. Seeds are produced in cones.

Slightly more advanced conifers show rather more variation in their tracheid structure. Conifers make normal tracheids in spring to carry the sudden increase in water flow as temperature and light increases the rate of transpiration. The walls are fairly thin. Later, as the need for water conducting tissue is declining, the newly formed tracheids grow longer as they develop and grow thicker walls to increase their support function. These are called fibre tracheids and form the later wood of the year. The rays of such trees are small and thin, usually one, or at most, two cells wide, very limited in height and not normally visible to the naked eye.

Timber from the conifer group of trees is called softwood to distinguish it from the hardwoods from more advanced trees, which have flowers and generally broader leaves. These terms are misnomers. Hardwoods and softwoods are in no way distinguished by their hardness. The softest wood is a hardwood (balsa) and some softwoods can be quite hard e.g. yew. Generally speaking, the hardwoods are harder but there are so many exceptions that I feel sure terminologists would like to change these terms were they not so firmly established.

Hardwoods are much more diverse and varied in their cell types and structural complexity. These plants developed fully enclosed seeds and insect attraction for pollen spreading, i.e. flowers, (many have since reverted to wind pollination but catkins are still flowers.) They also evolved leaves of much larger area to compete more efficiently for light. Such leaves transpire more water so the xylem had to evolve to supply water at a faster rate. Xylem vessels evolved alongside tracheids to cope with the faster maximum flow rates.

Hardwoods, therefore, consist of four or five cell types with some further possible subdivisions. The vascular cambium cells of hardwoods are much shorter than those of softwoods, generally less than 1 millimetre. Where these cells give rise to vessels, they do not usually elongate as they develop but they may enlarge laterally to give a short but very wide cell which, as explained on page 9, lose all contents and endwalls to become water-carrying tubes. With less endwall structure and greater diameter than tracheids, these carry water with less friction and, therefore, faster.

Broadleaved trees do not dispense with tracheids. Tracheids can carry water at an angle to the axis and they are a sort of insurance policy. Vessels may become useless if the water column in them breaks. This can happen because of insect boring or even wind stress at

Fig. 17 *Oak – showing vessels cut open.*

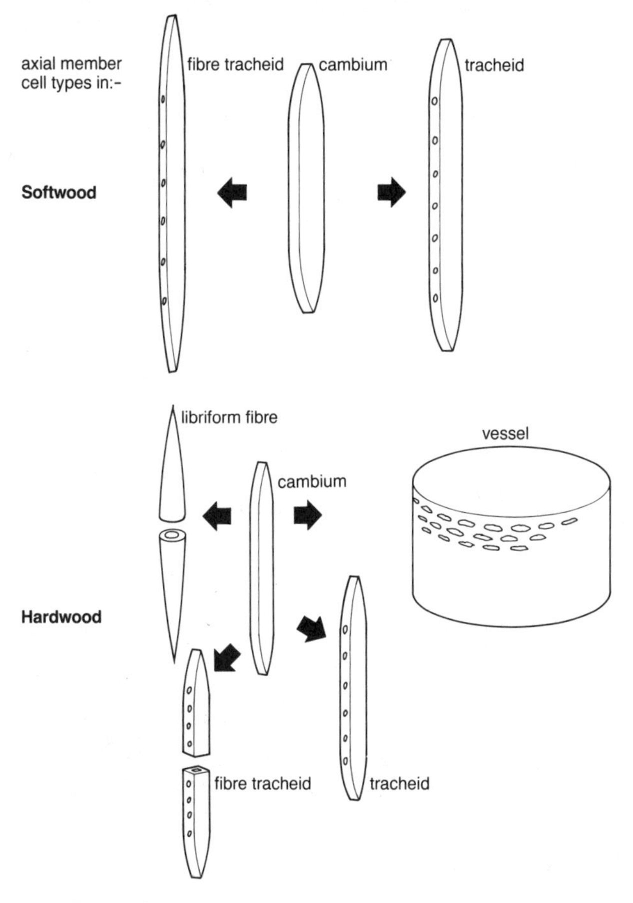

Fig. 18 *Axial member cell types.*

the tops of trees. Tracheids do not rely on continuous columns of water and so do not suffer from this problem. Hardwood tracheids are much shorter than those of conifers and enlarge comparatively little in diameter from the cambium cell that formed them, although most grow somewhat in length before final development into water conducting strands. Tracheids grade into fibre tracheids which are longer and thicker-walled, and generally produced later in the growing season. Before the end of the growth year, this trend continues and the output of the cambium produces cells which elongate far beyond the size of the initial cambium cell which produced them. These are called libriform fibres. They have lignin thickening which almost fill the cavity and are purely structural. They are the longest of the xylem cells of hardwood being typically 1.5 – 2 mm, exceptionally 4 – 5mm. These lengths are modest by softwood standards. It is this general difference in xylem cell length which explains the preference for softwoods for paper making.

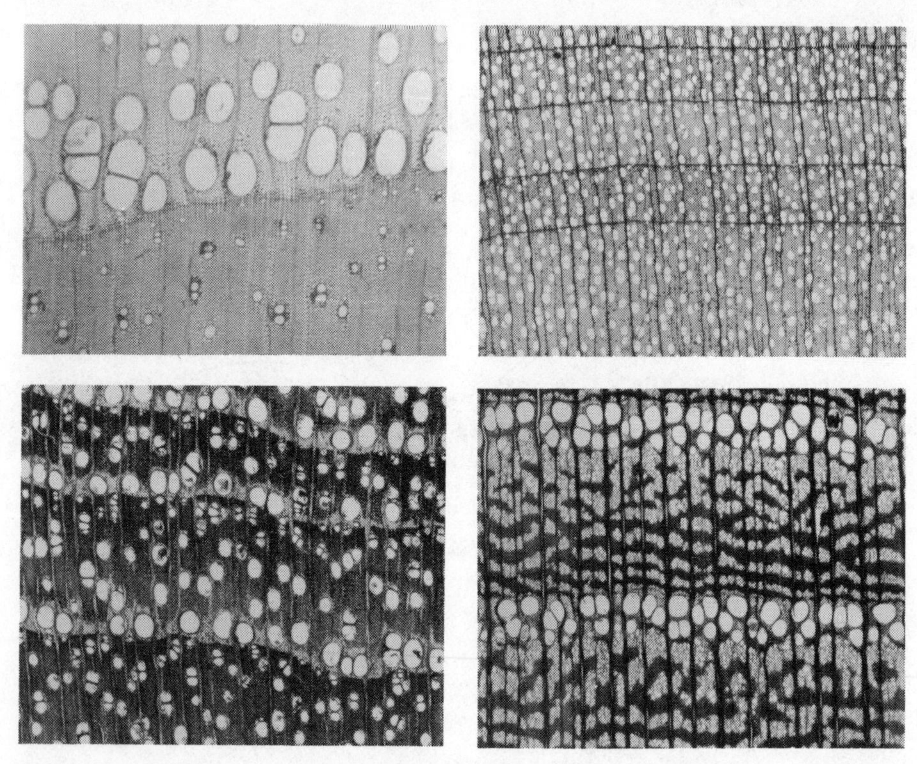

Fig. 19 *(top left) Ash. (top right) Birch. (bottom left) Teak. (bottom right) Elm.*

The changes from one cell type to another through the season may be gradual or quite abrupt. This can have quite marked visual effects (see Chapter Five). Hardwoods vary in the timing of their vessel production. Some produce all their vessels in one burst in spring and thereafter only make the smaller xylem cells. This is true of ash. Some produce vessels of more or less even size throughout the growing season such as beech, birch and willow. Another type produces vessels of steadily decreasing size through the year's growth. These include teak and American chestnut. Elm derives its characteristic and easily recognised structure from a ring of vessels at the start of the growth year followed by three or more almost simultaneous bursts of small vessels as the season progresses (see Chapter Five).

The pattern with all the vessels large and early is called 'ring-porous'. Simple ring-porous woods, such as ash and sweet chestnut, are easy to recognise with coarse textured pores accentuating their annual rings. Timbers with vessels evenly distributed are said to be 'diffuse-porous' and tend to have much smaller vessels – harder to see on the surface of the endgrain. As you can see from the above descriptions, to try to classify all timbers into either diffuse- or ring-porous would be to oversimplify the situation.

Along with increased diversity of their water conducting elements hardwoods have a more complex parenchyma system. Parenchyma cells retain living contents and form a network to transport and store more complex chemicals. In most softwoods, axial parenchyma is very limited or absent. In hardwood it is considerably more extensive and forms patterned networks already referred to (page 11). It is in the size and structure of the radial systems that hardwoods reach their greatest diversity. Softwoods have tiny rays with very little parenchyma in them. Often they are mainly tracheids running at 90 degrees to the rest.

Hardwood rays do not have tracheids in them but are composed entirely of parenchyma cells with living contents. In some, the rays are very small and limited; hardly greater in extent than softwoods. Willows, chestnut, poplar and ramin have rays which are uniseriate or one cell wide. Ash has many small rays which are biseriate at their widest point. If you look at cross sections of these timbers, you can miss the full extent of the rays as they taper off to nothing top and bottom. Descriptions of rays are more appropriate from the tangential viewpoint. Imagine looking at the outside of a freshly barkstripped trunk and seeing the rays end on at the point nearest to you. Seen from this view, uni- and biseriate rays are almost always invisible to the naked eye. They may just be visible with a good hand lens but they are really a microscope study feature. The larger rays are called multi-seriate. These can be up to thirty cells, half a millimetre wide and several centimetres long. Such rays are usually clearly visible. When trying to distinguish timbers as to species, these rays must be looked at under a microscope to decide whether the ray cells are all of one type or not. This is a microscope procedure beyond the scope of this book.

Figs. 20(a) and (b) *Oak showing two sizes of ray (arrowed).*

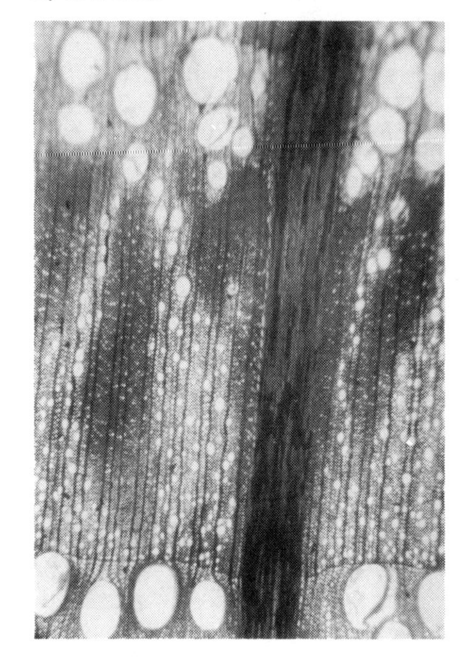

Many timbers have such obvious visual effects created by the sizes and colours of the rays that they become instantly recognisable. The slightly irregularly-spaced brown rays in beech make it easily recognised on almost any cut surface. The very regular and distinct rays of London plane, which give it the name of lacewood, are unmistakable. Rays reach perhaps their greatest extent in the various oaks. English oak has rays several centimetres high and about half a millimetre wide. The structures of which they are made are so different from their axial wood that they stand out, particularly when larger areas of them are exposed on a cut surface due to the different way they reflect light (see Chapter Five).

Seen in cross-section, rays never branch. In some timbers, however, they are seen to branch in the tangential view and run off at angles into other rays top and bottom. These are called 'aggregate rays'. The only common timber which shows this feature is hornbeam. The radial system is very interesting in this timber but, being very much the same colour and appearance as the axial system, it is not visually exciting.

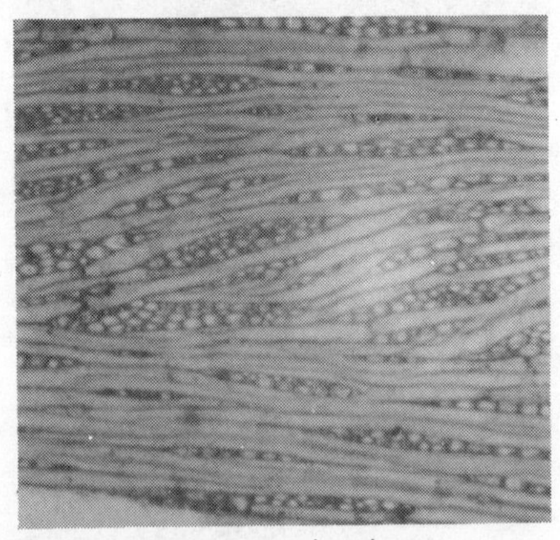

Fig. 21 *Aggregate rays – hornbeam.*

The function of the rays is to store and transport more complex materials. The storage of starch has already been described in Chapter One. It must be remembered that rays increase in number as the tree expands because the cambium initiates new rays every year.

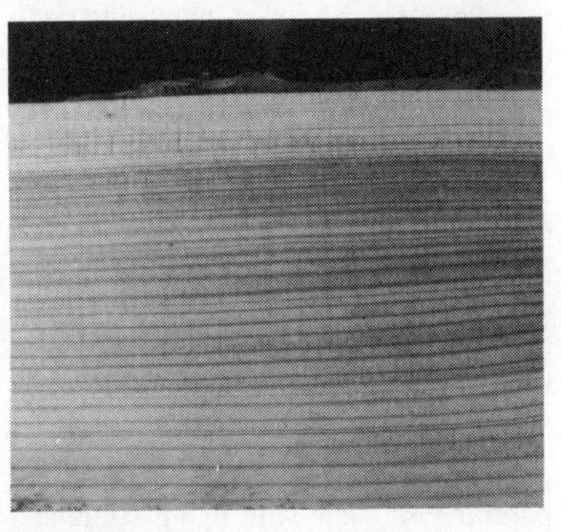

Fig. 22 *Larch showing sapwood and heartwood.*

Therefore some rays extend from the surface through only one year's growth, some through two years etc. A few go down to the centre. The central part of the trunk may be distinguishable from the surface layers by virtue of a darker colour. The central area will be called the heartwood, and the lighter outer part, the sapwood.

The tree has two methods of excretion, that is getting rid of the poisonous waste chemicals that all living activity produces. They can throw them away with the leaves at the end of each growing season, and this is partly responsible for the beautiful colours they may show at this time. They can also turn them into materials which can be harmlessly dumped in the centre of the trunk. Since these materials have some toxicity, there they may serve the useful purpose of rendering the central core, no longer used for transport, less attractive to wood-consuming insects and fungi. The heartwood is always considerably more pest-resistant than the sapwood (see Chapter Five). The living ray cells are essential to transport these substances inward, converting them to appropriate chemical forms on the way and then to dump them either in the innermost ray cells or into empty vessels (see Chapter Six).

Some of the rays in sapwood are transporting wastes inward and some store food in the dormant season. Such is the complexity of living cytoplasm that a given cell may be doing both. Some rays may be regarded as storage only where they do not extend in as far as the heartwood. Sapwood, therefore, may be assumed to have living parenchyma while the heartwood parenchyma may be mostly dead. Whether this also applies to the axial parenchyma seems even less certain. Some trees do not appear to have heartwood, eg ash, but this is due to it not differing from sapwood in colour. In other timbers the difference in colour at the heart/sapwood boundary can be quite spectacular. Padauk for example, as seen in many veneer pieces, changes from straw-coloured to an almost crimson red. Pau rosa is similar. Yew can also show a beautiful change. The heartwood may be very wide and almost fill the trunk with a thin layer of sapwood e.g. larch or it may be a small amount with wide sapwood e.g. pine.

The sapwood may have all its parenchyma alive and lack heartwood chemical impregnation, but it is not all transporting water. Dr David Bellamy conducted an experiment for one of his television programmes during which an oak tree was held up by scaffolding and then cut through near ground level. A trough of water was inserted for the trunk to use as a water supply and its uptake could therefore be monitored day and night. At night, with leaf pores closed, it absorbed water relatively slowly but during the day its water demand was very heavy. A larch, treated similarly, transported much less water. Larch is a softwood with tracheids only and reduced area leaves. After a time, Dr. Bellamy introduced the brightly coloured metabolic poison, picric acid. This was taken up but did not slow the water loss, proving that this section of the water transport does not rely on living tissue activity. Its significance to sapwood function could be seen when the trunk was cut into well above the level of the water in the trough. Only the current year's growth was stained orange. It seems, therefore, that in many trees only the newly-produced xylem transports water. The rest of the sapwood may act as a reservoir as the hollow xylem certainly seems to be water-filled. If it does serve this function, the living ray cells may be essential to transport water out to the current year's xylem to top it up, since water cannot easily pass across annual rings which may be largely libriform fibres.

Dr. Bellamy's experiment can be repeated on a small scale if a side branch of several years' growth can be sacrificed. Cut it when the tree is in full leaf, keeping the cut surface thoroughly wet during the cutting. In full daylight, put it into a container of some bright, water-soluble dye. Ink may be suitable – red is best. Leave it for an hour or two and then cut the stem across at least six inches above the level of the ink. You should then be able to decide for yourself how much of the sapwood xylem is functional in water transport in that species. This can be tried on different species however they may not all react the same way.

CHAPTER 3

CONVERSION TO TIMBER

A freshly-felled and trimmed tree stem may, in a few cases, be used as it is. This would only apply to small-diameter trunks (sometimes called 'roundwood') but includes a number of rural crafts seldom practised today. More usually, it is converted by sawing it longitudinally into square-edged sections. Planks, battens and laths are terms commonly used while baulks, deals, staves and scantlings are terms less often heard to describe the different sizes and proportions of such sections of converted timber.

Fig. 23 *Pit sawing.*

The sawing was originally done by two men with a long two handled rip-saw working with the log held over a pit. The colloquialisms 'top dog' and 'under dog' derive from this working method. Today, this job is done by mechanical means usually with a large bandsaw, although circular saws and chainsaws can be utilised.

To produce the best from the log requires skill, experience and an understanding of the structures likely to be found within the trunk of a tree. It also requires some knowledge of the changes which will take place in the material during seasoning.

The trunk is a tapering cylindrical structure made of layers of annual growth rings whose nature depends on species. It may or may not be clean, straight, and without side branches, but the remains of previous branches in the form of knots will be present somewhere within the timber. These will probably be in a fairly regular pattern if it is a softwood but less regular and pre-

Fig. 24 *Converting elm on a bandsaw. Note the heavy roller moving table.*

dictable in a hardwood species. The sawyer who can read the shape of the log and the figure of each piece as it comes off, is likely to make the best of the material and protect his sawblade from damage. The direction of knots, with respect to the proportions of the pieces in which they occur, is of paramount importance to their strength and hence the financial return on the trunk.

Longitudinal cuts with a bandsaw are tangential or radial. Tangentially-cut timber is described as 'flat sawn' 'slash sawn' or as sawn 'through and through'. If a whole log is converted in this way into boards, then one or two at the centre will be radial sections. All would include part of the trunk circumference as 'wane' or 'waney edge'. Hardwoods converted in this country are mostly flat sawn. Because of the regular occurrence of softwood sidebranches, flat-sawing all through would leave some planks

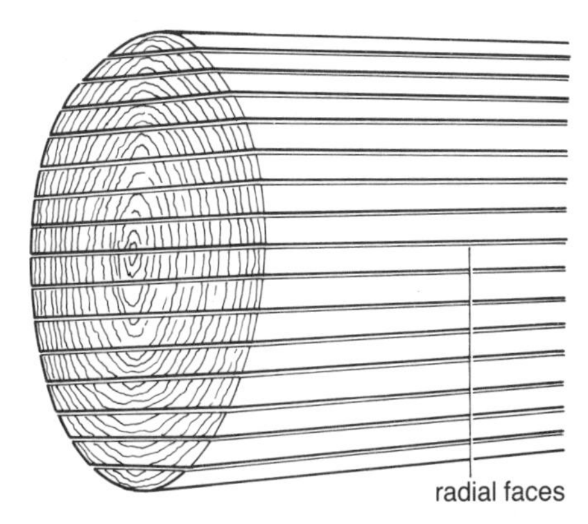

Fig. 25 *Sawing 'through and through'.*

Fig. 26 *The direction of the knot severely weakens this plank.*

with knots running straight across, destroying their potential strength. Many different sawing patterns can be adopted to avoid knots running through sections in a way that seriously weakens them. The majority of softwood is imported already-converted. For special purposes, particularly chosen logs may be sawn so that more of the sections are nearly radial. This may be done for example with oak to accentuate the 'silver grain' pattern of the large rays. There are various patterns of cutting to achieve this with minimum waste of timber and time.

Truly radial sawing of whole logs is expensive in time and wasted timber where flat sections are required, since this method naturally produces feather-edged boards. Most timber intended for stringed musical instruments is produced in this way. It gives the least possible distortion on seasoning, makes the most of any 'fiddleback' grain pattern, and is most productive of the tonal qualities for which the instrument maker strives. Tone woods for the bowed, stringed instruments are almost entirely selected North European maple and spruce. Conversion for this purpose is a specialism carried out mostly in West

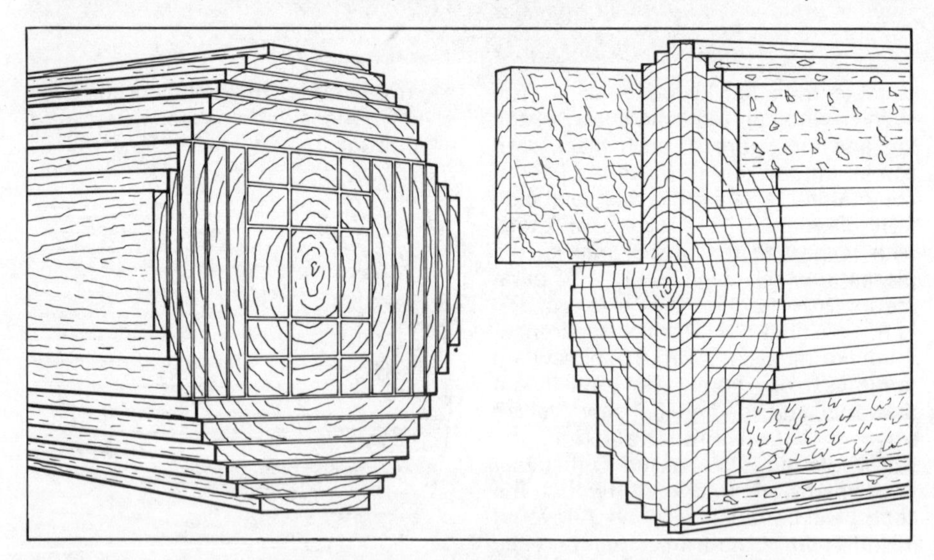

Fig. 27 *(above left) Conversion of softwood to avoid knots running across planks.*
Fig. 28 *Cutting to maximise radial faces e.g. for oak to show silver grain.*

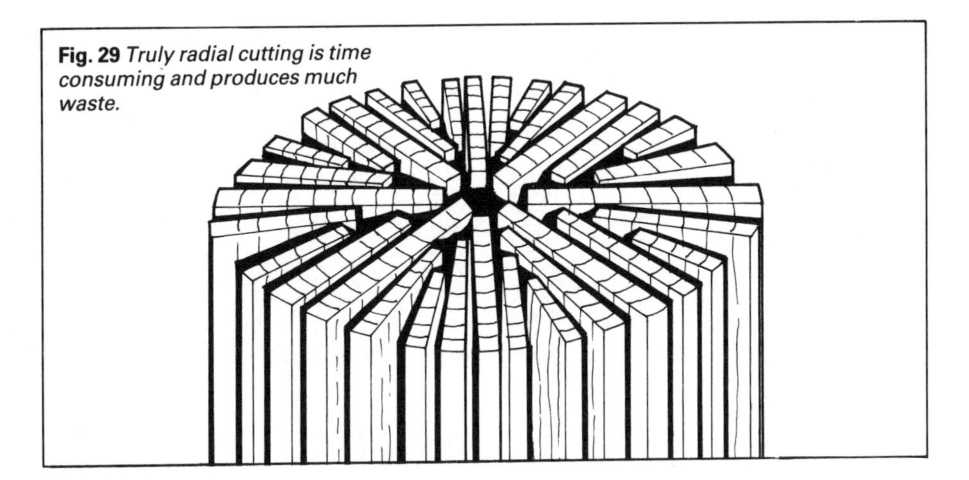
Fig. 29 *Truly radial cutting is time consuming and produces much waste.*

Germany and such materials are among the most expensive of timbers.

In most cases of special figuring in hardwoods, the radially-cut surface is to be preferred as the patterns seen are often due to significant rays as in oak, or regular grain direction changes as in sapele. Timbers without attractive rays may look more figured when cut tangentially where they have obvious annual rings e.g. ash or Douglas fir. Softwoods generally are more highly figured on tangential surfaces as they have minute rays. Many of the tropical hardwoods without significant rings, rays or grain variations will be little affected in appearance by the angle of cut e.g. jelutong or iroko (see Chapter Five).

All timber sections shrink on drying from about 30% moisture content by weight. This is known as 'fibre saturation point' (see Chapter Seven). Problems arise here due to the fact that shrinkage is not uniform. All timbers shrink more in the tangential direction than they do radially. Tangential shrinkage is typically between 1.25 and 2 times the radial shrinkage. These figures relate to the dimensional shrinkage on drying from green timber to 12% water by weight. In practice, this does not start until the timber is already dried to 28 – 30%.

This means that almost any section that can be cut will change cross-sectional shape on drying. If the log is left to season in the round, it is highly likely to develop major splits along its length called 'shakes'. One or more radial or cross shakes is almost inevitable. Heart or star shakes may form from the centre.

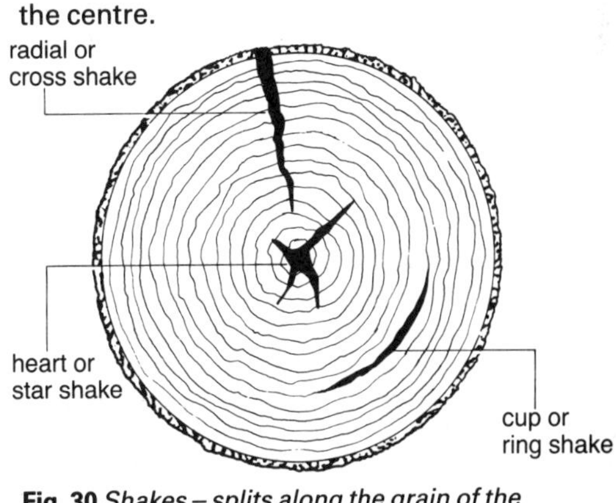

Fig. 30 *Shakes – splits along the grain of the log.*

Fig. 31 *Heart shake in oak – a problem for the sawyer.*

There are two clear reasons for the difference in shrinkage, and some less clear ones. The first reason is that timber shrinkage is lateral. Most of the cellulose molecules in the wood are axially arranged and, as water evaporates from between them, they get closer together but not shorter. (Longitudinal shrinkage of timber is very small and is often described as negligible. For most purposes this is true but it depends on the structure made from it.) A structure which mixes brick or stone with long lengths of timber may suffer on drying, as the length shrinkage is not zero. (It can generally be ignored for all-wood structures). The cellulose in the rays is arranged radially to the trunk, and therefore shrinks negligibly while the axial members around them are trying to shrink more. Since these systems are firmly linked in sound timber, rays should inhibit radial shrinkage. Therefore the radial shrinkage of oak (3.5% approx) is decreased while its tangential

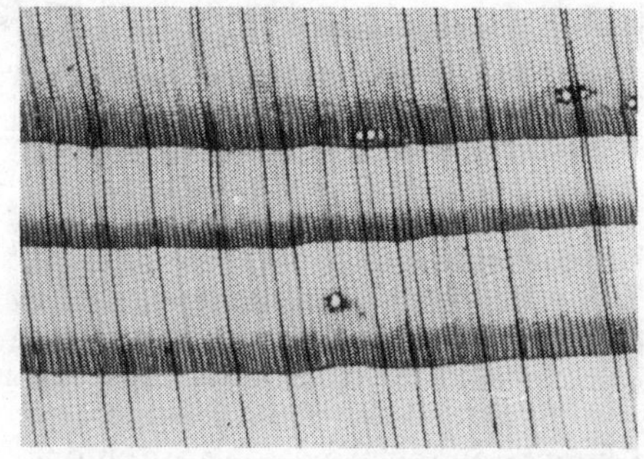

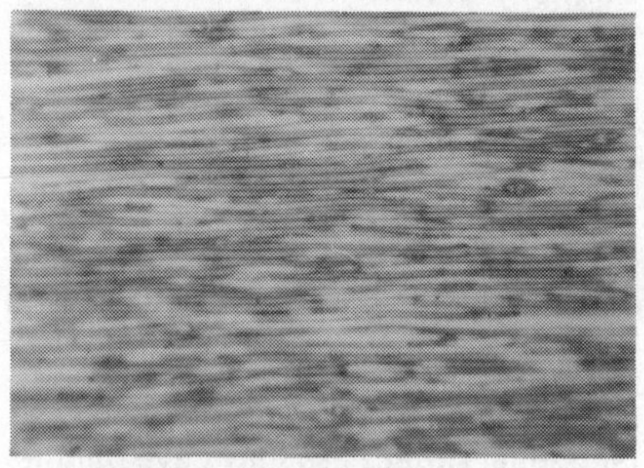

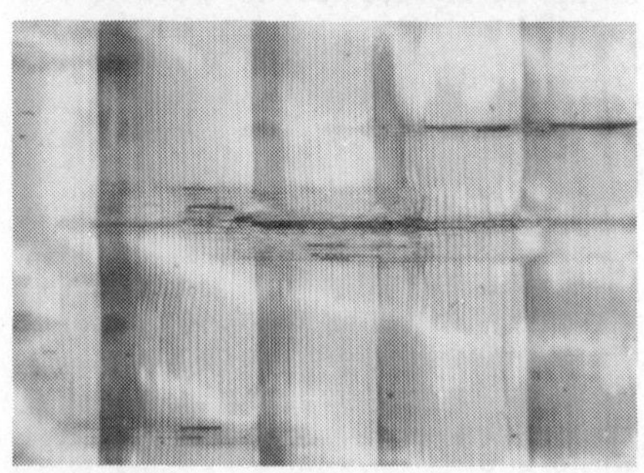

Fig. 32(a) *Pine – cross section.*
Fig. 32(b) *Pine – tangential section.*
Fig. 32(c) *Pine – radial section showing ray with a marked resin canal.*

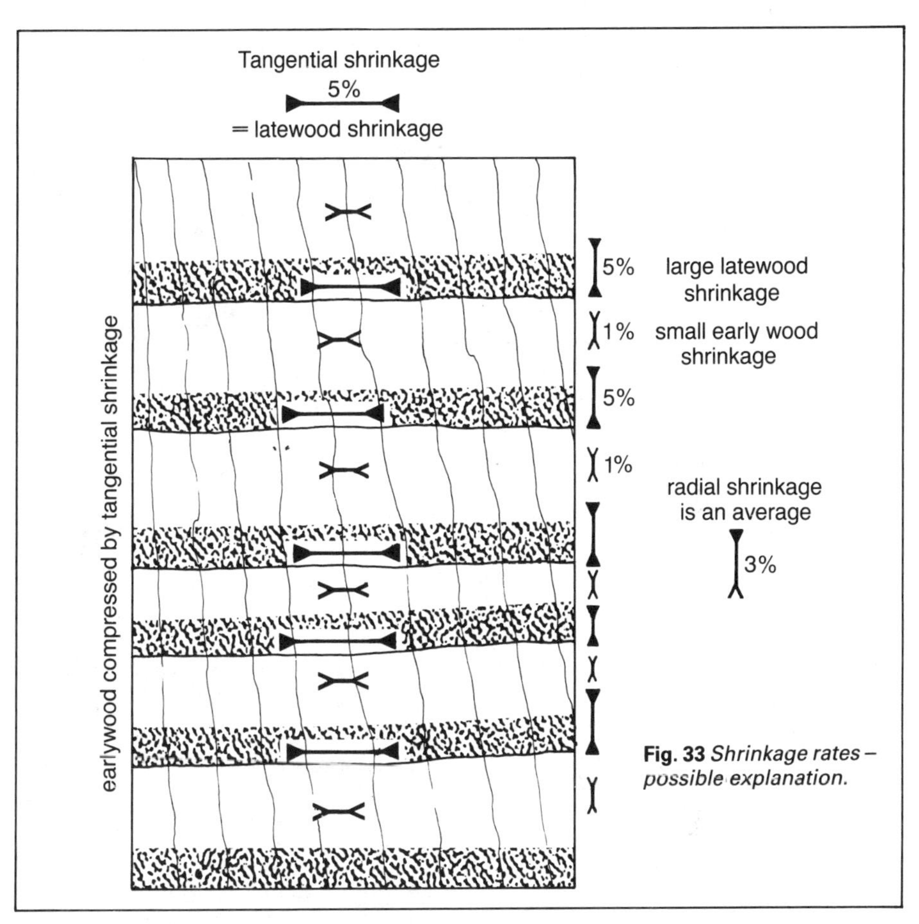

Fig. 33 *Shrinkage rates – possible explanation.*

shrinkage (7% approx) is unimpeded.

Some timbers, however, have a much less significant radial system. Pine has a minimal volume of radial fibres but follows the same general pattern of shrinkage. This is due to the variation of texture across the season's growth in a ring. Earlywood is relatively thin-walled while, outside this, the latewood is composed of fibres with much thicker walls. Being more solid material with less space, the latewood shrinks more than the earlywood. In the tangential direction, the powerful shrinkage of the latewood layers will compress the less substantial earlywood between them. In the radial direction, each layer is more free to shrink by a different amount. Therefore the tangential shrinkage of pine (5% approx.) is the considerable shrinkage of its latewood. The smaller radial shrinkage (3% approx.) is presumably an average between latewood and earlywood shrinkage values. The same may apply to ash and sweet chestnut.

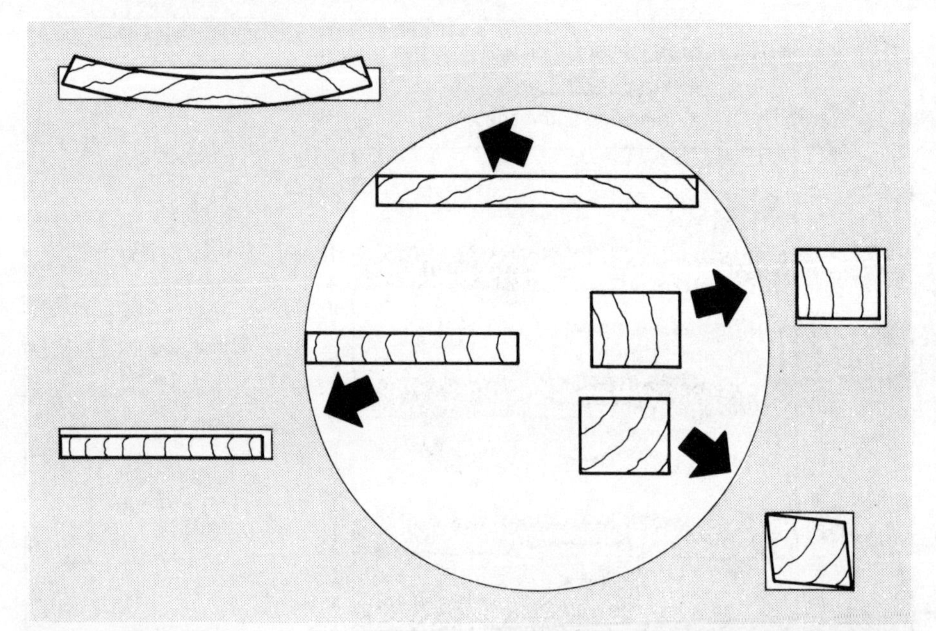

Fig. 34 *Shape changes due to shrinkage.*

This explanation may leave one wondering about diffuse-porous hardwoods where these have limited ray development. Almost all timbers produce some thicker-walled xylem cells toward autumn, so the above argument may apply. Shrinkage levels in timber vary enormously. Afzelia has about the lowest values (rad. – 1% tan – 1.5%) with teak, iroko and afrormosia not much higher. Plane (lacewood), with its well developed ray system, shows a marked difference in shrinkage (rad 4% tan 9–10%) as does keruing (rad. – 3% tan 7–8%). The greatest difference in shrinkage rates is recorded for virola (rad. – 2.5% tan – 9%). When one looks at this timber under the microscope with the above explanations in mind, it is difficult to see why. It seems likely that some of the difference between radial and tangential shrinkage values is concerned with specific orientations of cellulose molecules within the cell walls of the xylem cells. As an electron microscope feature, this is beyond the scope of this book.

Fig. 35 *Plum – this piece was cut square.*

The difference in shrinkage rates changes the shape of the sections cut from a log. Generally, planks will curve away from the centre of the original trunk. Square sections will become rectangular or diamond-shaped, depending on annual ring direction. Radially-cut planks will change shape the least but, of course, involve higher levels of wastage.

It is assumed in this argument that the axial fibres of the trunk run accurately axial. This will not always be so. Tree trunks are not perfect cylinders. Knots will be present in some parts of the interior of the trunk and are anything but axial. The axial fibres run at angles around the knot, compromising the overall strength. It may be that the grain of the wood runs spirally around the trunk. This is found more often in some species than others, but reduces the strength of any long piece due to highly-angled grain.

The sawyer has the responsibility of converting the log into the most suitable sections, having regard to the position of knots and grain direction. This may be relatively straightforward if the forester has trimmed sidebranches to reduce the extent of dead knots, but this is not always the case. The more recent outer wood will probably be free of these and will be taken off tangentially as planking. This may then reveal the extent and direction of knots present and, assuming that the manoeuvering equipment is to hand, the log can be turned to cut to best advantage. Some smaller timberyards have limited equipment and facility to repeatedly turn large logs where necessary, and would not

Fig. 36 *(above) The bark on this trunk strongly suggests spiral grain – whitebeam.*
Fig. 36 *(below). Spirally grained cherry is only useful for making small items.*

attempt the more complex cutting shown in Figs 27 and 28.

The direction of the grain, and extent and direction of knots present, are taken into account in the grading of timber into different qualities appropriate to different types of use. Since this is done by an experienced person purely by eye, it is known as visual grading.

There are a number of different grading systems. The Russian and Scandinavian systems are similar and applied to much of the softwood sold in this country. There are five or six grades, although the top three grades are generally included together under the slightly misleading term 'unsorted'. The specification of grades includes 'knot area ratio' [KAR]. For the best grades this is 1/6 on the face and 1/12 on the edge. Skilled cutting maximises the amount of unsorted (i.e. grades 1, 2 & 3) timber available from a log. Later reconversion in your workshop to smaller sizes can downgrade timber if it is not done with equal understanding and skill. KAR values of 1/3 on the face or 1/6 on the edge grades it down to 5th grade.

The amount of 'wane' present (unsquared parts of the circumference) is also taken into account in visual grading, as are the extent of surface splits and checks. This Russian/Scandinavian system specification is a bit vague on the angle of grain which is acceptable within each grade. Most of the other systems specify grain to face or edge slope angles for each grade. Therefore B.S. 4978 top grade S.S. (special structural) specifies 1/10 maximum grain angle while the lower G.S. (general structural) accepts 1/6. This grain angle would fail all the American ALS system grades which specify 1/12 for the 'select' grade down to 1/8 for the lowest acceptable structural grade. Full details and comparison tables are available from T.R.A.D.A. and Southern and Western Forest Products Association (USA) (see acknowledgements; see also stress grading, Chapter Four).

An even older conversion method than sawing still has its uses. Many timbers can usefully be converted for certain purposes by splitting (also sometimes called 'cleaving' or 'riving'). This requires splitting wedges of metal and a sledgehammer to deal with trunks or an axe and a billhook for smaller sections. The original tools for this operation included the axe-like 'handled wedge' and the giant mallet called a 'beetle'. The 'froe' was another tool but one which bears little resemblance to anything commonly seen today.

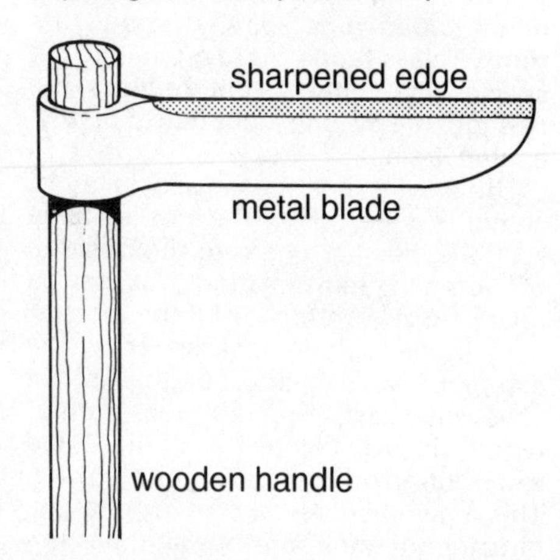

Fig. 37 *The froe – a tool for the controlled splitting of wood.*

This was the method by which beech was turned into the blanks from which Windsor chair legs were traditionally made, prior to turning on a pole lathe. The backsticks of these chairs were of ash for preference, although beech, oak, elm and yew have all been used. In order to be long and slender, but take the side

Fig. 38 *Mike Abbott – one of the leading exponents of the use of green timber – here splitting sweet chestnut with 'beetle' and metal wedges.*

stress, these parts had to be split to ensure that the grain ran parallel to the piece before rounding with draw knife and 'stail engine'.

Splitting green timber, such as ash, successfully in good lengths with minimal wastage requires considerable skill in handling the tool and directing the split by careful side-stress on the piece of timber as the tool is pushed forward and levered sideways. Intimate knowledge of the species in use and the sample to hand is essential. Timber converted in this way will always provide maximum possible strength in very small cross sections. In the turning of lace bobbins, for example, split timber must be more successful than the squared saw-cut blanks so commonly available.

The lines along which timber splits most easily are the rays and the earlywood lines, especially in ring-porous timbers like ash and sweet chestnut. Chestnut was a favourite timber for agricultural and domestic purposes in years gone by, both because of its naturally fairly high level of durability (see Chapter Eight) and its ease of splitting along rays in one direction (even though these are small) and the earlywood lines in the other. Split chestnut is still commonly to be seen made into a type of fencing. The durability of any timber is greater when split because there are few exposed vessel ends to allow water to infiltrate. Many of the rural crafts of yesteryear are based on splitting as the main conversion method and coppiced English timbers, such as hazel and hawthorn, in addition to those already described.

A related technique used by the North American Indians involved hammering wet ash (usually American black ash) until the earlywood vessels collapsed and the wood could be stripped into single layers of the very tough latewood. These had several uses and could be woven like palm leaves into the most robust basketwork imaginable. This is rather too labour-intensive a method to contemplate today.

Another completely different way of taking a tree apart into usable materials is 'veneer cutting'. Originally, veneers were cut using a saw and, in this way, a small amount of very expensive and

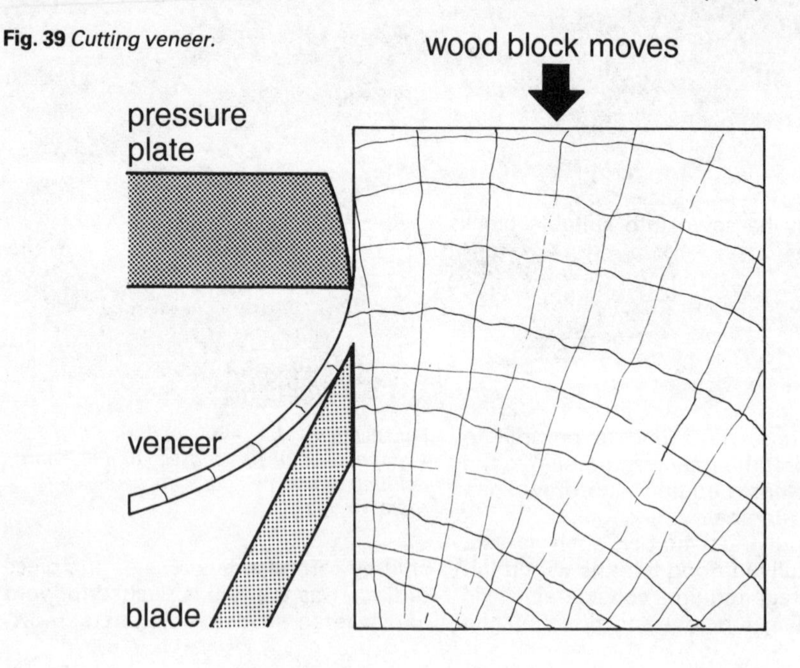

Fig. 39 *Cutting veneer.*

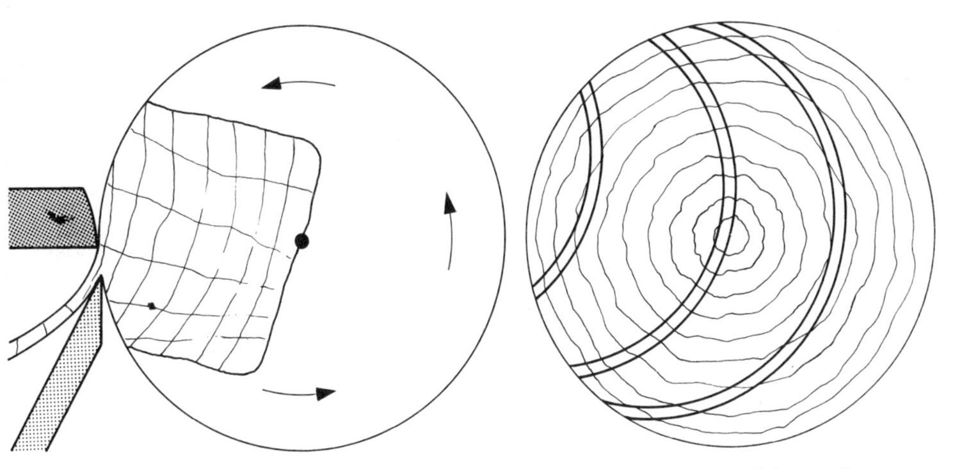

Fig. 40 *(left) Rotary veneer cutting – gives patterns which would be impossible on a flat surface,* ***Fig 41*** *(right).*

usually imported wood was made to cover a piece of furniture. Veneers can still be cut in this way today by anyone with an accurate bandsaw or circular saw. This creates the problem of wasting as much timber as it produces. Some veneers are still saw cut where the timber is extremely hard, e.g. lignum vitae and some types of ebony. More modern veneer production cuts the timber by knife blade leaving no kerf wastage. The log may be sawn into suitable blocks which are then treated by steam or hot water to soften them; they are then cut by a machine with a blade and a pressure plate, the whole having some of the properties of the mouth of a plane.

The block of wood may be moved straight up and down, advancing by the veneer thickness at each stroke. This will give a section of the flat face of the piece and therefore equate to a normally-cut timber surface. Veneer cutting is not limited to flat cutting however. Other types of veneer cutting machines are rotary, the timber revolving around an axis like wood in a lathe. The wood being cut does not have to be fixed at its own centre but can be off-centre in a variety of ways. This can give a figure pattern on the veneer which would be impossible on a flat solid wood surface. Veneers cut in this way are usually decorative and

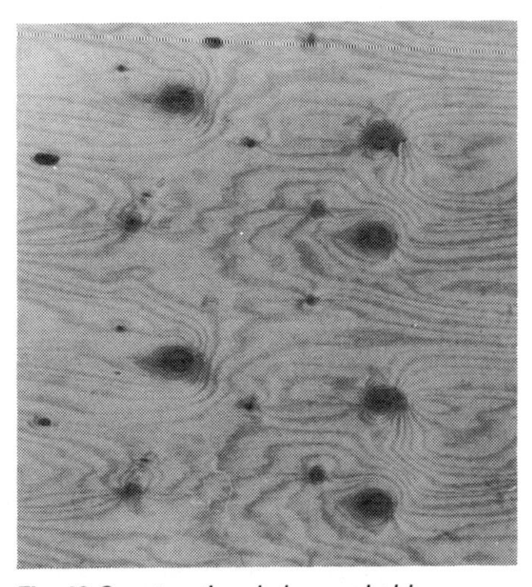

Fig. 42 *Constructional ply – probably Douglas fir, obviously rotary cut.*

less than 1mm thick. They are available in an enormous range of exotic species and are a specialist supply market. Most of these veneers are now cut in their country of origin to add value to the product. This is of obvious worth where timbers are highly prized for their figure but scarce (see Chapters Five and Nine).

Another related method of veneer cutting is the rotary continuous cutting of logs for plywood construction. The log is rotated from its own centre and cut by a knife that advances one veneer thickness per revolution. In this way, continuous sheets of considerable size may be obtained which are tangential sections at all points. Such veneers may be from less than 1mm to over 4mm. The regular pattern of sidebranch formation can look very odd when it is repeated almost like a wallpaper pattern, as can be seen so often in builder's constructional ply.

CHAPTER 4

STRENGTH PROPERTIES OF WOOD

The strength properties of wood depend to a large extent on structures which are beyond the range of the normal microscope. The individual cells of wood are glued together with hemi-cellulose and pectin and are composed of lignified cellulose tubes. Cellulose is laid down first as a distinctly fibrous structure and is then impregnated and overlaid by the more rigid and amorphous material lignin. These cell wall materials convey different properties. The combination is similar to reinforced concrete, or perhaps a better analogy is fibreglass. The cellulose fibres, like the glass fibres, make a tough but flexible framework which the lignin, like the plastic resin, renders more rigid and coherent. The cellulose alone is floppy. The lignin alone would be as brittle as unreinforced resin. These chemicals we cannot see, with the exception that cellulose fibres can be seen with an electron microscope.

What we do see when we look at a timber very closely is the arrangement and sizes of the tubular structure. We see the sizes of the vessels, if any, the packing of the narrower tracheids and fibres and the extent of the radial system. In some cases, we can infer some of a timber's strength properties from its visible structures. So, for example, timbers which are ring-porous, with good development of latewood fibres, tend to be tough with considerable shock resistance (ash and hickory). In most other cases, the properties are dependent on submicroscopic features. It would be difficult to predict purely on structure, even under the microscope, that afzelia has the lowest shrinkage rate of almost any known timber. A close look at the *Aceraceae* family of timbers would be hard put to reveal that rock maple is one of the most abrasion-resistant timbers while the soft maples and sycamore are definitely not.

The single most significant feature of any timber, with respect to its strength properties, is the proportion of the whole which is actually lignified cellulose. Apart from resins and gums etc. (see Chapter Six), a well-seasoned timber is almost entirely lignified cellulose and air. The proportion of solid material to air is responsible for a timber's density and many of its general strength properties.

Density is quoted in several different units. Perhaps the commonest is the ratio of the weight of a given volume of timber to the weight of the same volume of water. This is called 'specific gravity' and, being a ratio, is quoted without units:

$$\text{Specific Gravity} = \frac{\text{Weight of X vol of timber}}{\text{Weight of X vol of water}}$$

Variations on this theme include densities quoted as weight per cubic foot. This is usually quoted in pounds imperial (water = 62.5 lb/ft^3). One may also find weight per cubic metres quoted in kilograms (water = 1000 kg per metre ^{3}). To convert, divide pounds weight by 62.5 or kilograms by 1000 and you have specific gravity.

Unfortunately, not all the quoted densities state the moisture content of the timber. Ideally, they should be quoted at 12% moisture content but it is not always so. Densities quoted as 'air dried' can be very misleading, and those without any qualification may be anything from green to 12% and are of little use. In any case there is a natural variability of density within each species which may depend on speed of growth and position of the specimen within the tree structure. Densities, quoted to three significant figures, as they sometimes are, suggest a precision which is just not applicable to a material as variable as wood. Even a second significant figure is of dubious relevance unless it relates to a particular specimen. Ideally the S.G. should be stated as + or − X%, but this is not general.

The density of the solid material in wood is from 1.5 to 1.6. The extent to which a wood is less dense than this is a measure of its air content. Not surprisingly many green timbers have S.G. values over 1 and therefore sink in fresh water. Teak is often ringed to allow some air drying before it is felled in order that it may be transportable by water. Even balsa, freshly felled, barely floats in water.

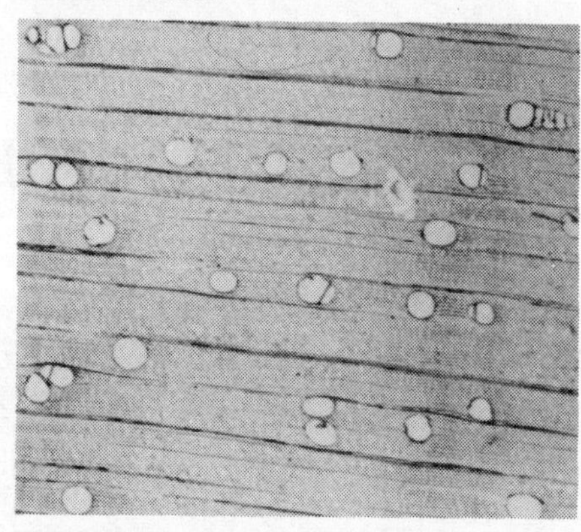

Fig. 43 *Balsa – cross section 90% air.*

Seasoned to 12% moisture content, balsa has an S.G. of about 0.15 which suggests that it is 90% air. At the other extreme is lignum vitae at approximately 1.1 – 1.2. It can be surprising when one first sees a wooden object sink! Ekki and greenheart can also be above 1 . Central American black ironwood (*Krugiodendron sp.*) is quoted at 1.4 but from a source which did not quote moisture content.

Normal timbers generally fall into the range 0.3 – 0.8. Many, though not all, of a timber's strength properties show considerable correlation with density but this is modified by the structural features of each timber. A simple statement of density alone does not give a strength measurement.

Wood is an 'anisotropic' material. That is, its strength is not the same in all directions. Wood can be broken in a wide variety of ways, so there are a wide variety of tests which can be applied to measure resistance to breaking forces. Obviously, for results to be comparable, tests have had to be standardised.

BENDING STRENGTH

This test takes a piece of timber 30×2×2 cm and slowly applies force to the middle until the piece breaks. This places the top of the piece in compression and the bottom in tension, so mechanically it is fairly complex. However, it is simple to apply and is directly related to the way timber may fail in use. It gives results in Newton's force applied per mm^2 of cross section, N/mm^2.

This is closely related to the test for stiffness, where the force needed to cause a certain deflection is measured, not the force needed to break the sample.

Fig. 44 *Bending strength testing machine.*

Generally, both of these properties show a considerable increase as the timber is seasoned from green to 12% moisture content. Related tests are applied to a timber when it is 'stress-graded'. Lengths of known cross-section timber are passed through a machine which applies a sidestress to the piece and measures its response in terms of deflection. This allows the wood to be reliably quoted for strength. The machine automatically sorts it into two main classes of strength – M75 or M50 – or rejects it as stress-graded timber. By using stress-graded timber, along with the span tables published by T.R.A.D.A., the structural designer can ensure adequate strength without wasting resources or space with oversized timbers.

Another stress grading category is the S.C. 1–9 grades classification where softwoods are generally in classes 3, 4 or 5, and classes 8 and 9 are occupied by timbers such as ekki or greenheart with colossal bending resistance.

TOUGHNESS

All the above relates to slowly-applied side forces but this does not encompass all the stresses placed upon timbers in use. Impact resistance testing is applied to the same sized piece as for the above test. A 1.5kg weight is dropped onto the piece from a certain height, established as that which will just break the piece or cause a 6cm. deflection. This value is actually one which decreases with seasoning in most timbers – hence some of the uses to which we can put green timber.

Both bending strength and toughness show a general correlation with timber density, although some timbers stand out with exceptional values. The toughness of ash for example is very high for its density but this test really reveals the exceptional nature of hickory as an impact tool handle material.

Elasticity is another property of timber. When it is deflected by a force and released, it will return to something approaching its previous shape. Some timbers spring back very well. A totally non-elastic timber would remain bent. Elasticity is another of the properties which increase on seasoning. Therefore, if some timbers are worked when green or have had their moisture replaced by steaming, they can be bent into shapes from which they do not recover when dried. Ash, beech and yew have all been used in this way to make the bent parts of Windsor chairs.

This cannot be done at all with some timbers. This technique manipulates the timbers' elasticity over a long timescale and with moisture content variation. In the short term, timbers may behave very differently. Riven yew is noted for its properties in the making of the longbow. Bows of other timbers can be made and pulled to the same 'weight' but do not spring back with the aggression of yew. Clearly, this is a property which depends not only on the visible form differences between timbers but also on invisible ultrastructural differences. Elasticity is only poorly correlated to density.

COMPRESSION

The obvious application of timber where compression resistance is important is as pit props in mining. A considerable amount of timber nationwide is used for this application. To test a timber's resistance to compression, a piece 6×2×2 cm. is stood on end and loaded very slowly (0.6 mm/minute) until it fails. This property of a timber is closely related to its density at 12% moisture and inversely related to its moisture content, green timber being weakest.

In all the above tests, knots will reduce

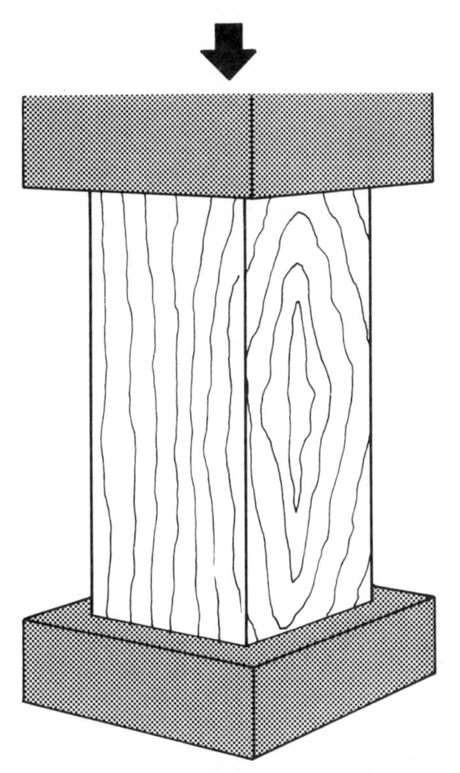
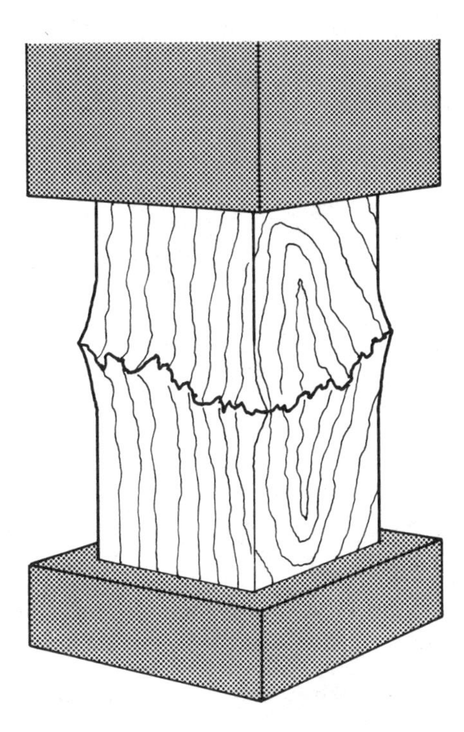

Fig. 45 *Compression testing.*

the ability of a timber to resist failure due to the deflections which knots cause in the grain direction and the amount of material in the knot running in directions not useful to the resistance of the force applied.

HARDNESS

Another useful property of timber is resistance to indentation. The experienced may find this out swiftly by using a fingernail. The scientific test takes a block of wood and forces a hardened steel ball into it. The standard test rig has a ball of 11.3 mm diameter and measures the force slowly applied to force the ball into the timber by the whole of its radius. An ingenious electrical contact alongside the ball switches on the machine recorder when this occurs. The test is repeated on radial and tangential faces. It is normally performed on knotless timber. The presence of knots actually increases this value in practice. It is another value which increases as timber loses water. Oak, of course, is noted for its performance in this test as anyone who has tried to drive nails into seasoned oak will realise. It is well correlated with density although some timbers, e.g. oak and rosewood, show values above those expected. Results are given in Newton's force.

This test also assumes a slow loading. Some short term stresses may cause different behaviour. Therefore a soft timber by the above test – willow – by a

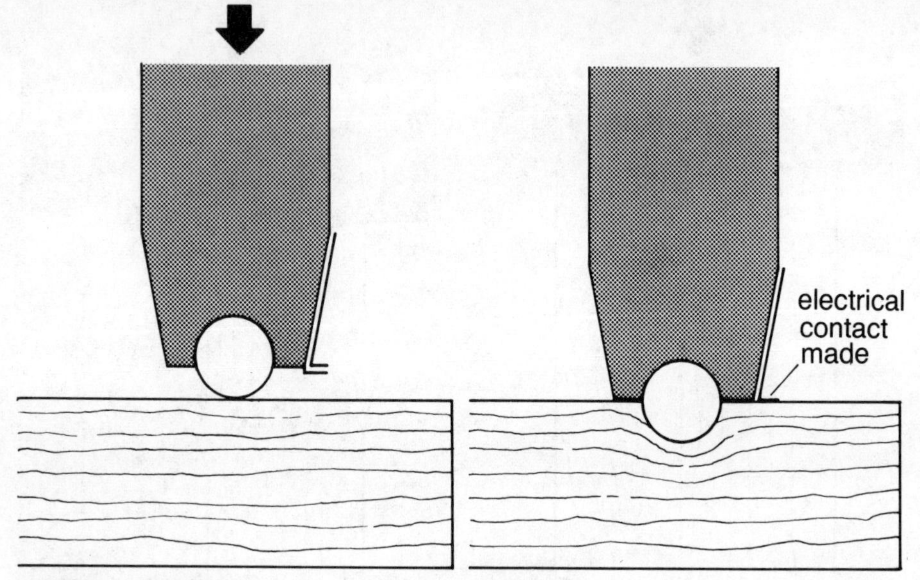

Fig. 46 *Hardness testing.*

special combination of elasticity and encapsulation of air in xylem elements shows short timescale hardness in resisting the indentation of cricket balls.

CLEAVABILITY AND SHEAR STRESS

Both of these stresses seek to separate the fibres in the wood. Cleavage testing takes a piece 4.5 × 2 × 2 cm and cuts a template shape out of it, as shown in Fig. 47. This allows the jaws of the test rig to gain a grip and pull the piece apart so that it splits along the grain. Shear testing takes a square piece of timber and

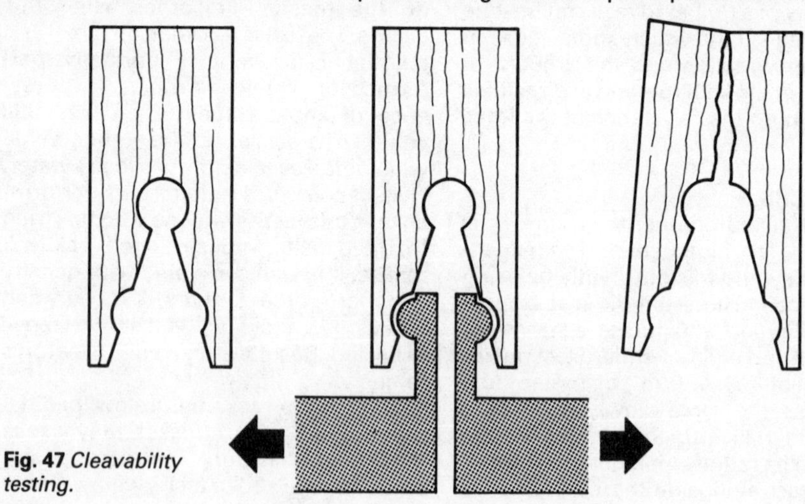

Fig. 47 *Cleavability testing.*

loads it offcentre as shown in Fig. 48.

For straight-grained timbers, this tests the materials which cause the fibres to adhere – the hemicellulose and pectins. Ramin is a particularly poor performer in this test.

It is much more strongly resisted by timbers, such as elm and some mahoganies, which are cross-grained.

Wood is also very strong in tension. Imagine trying to break a small twig by a straight pull. This property is less important in practice because wooden members in tension in a structure are overwhelmingly likely to fail at their points of attachment rather than in the middle.

All of the strength property tests, when performed repeatedly, show variations which can be graphed as shown in Fig. 49. The lower values as at X–X are those which must be taken into account by the designer of a structure.

Each tree has a certain genetic constitution arrived at by evolution with some elements of random chance. This will specify the range of conditions under which it can grow at a maximum rate. It will grow more slowly as conditions depart from this ideal. These conditions can profoundly affect the nature of the timber produced. In softwoods, generally, less suitable conditions and therefore slow growth will reduce the amount of the thinner-walled earlywood produced. Proportionately, more of the growth will be denser latewood fibre-tracheids. Slower-grown softwoods tend to be denser and therefore stronger in those properties which correlate with density although there are limits to this. Very poor conditions cause poor growth which will be weaker. Rapidly grown softwood is of lower density and may only be suitable for paper pulp or similar industrial uses. The optimum varies for each timber but is typically 8–20 rings

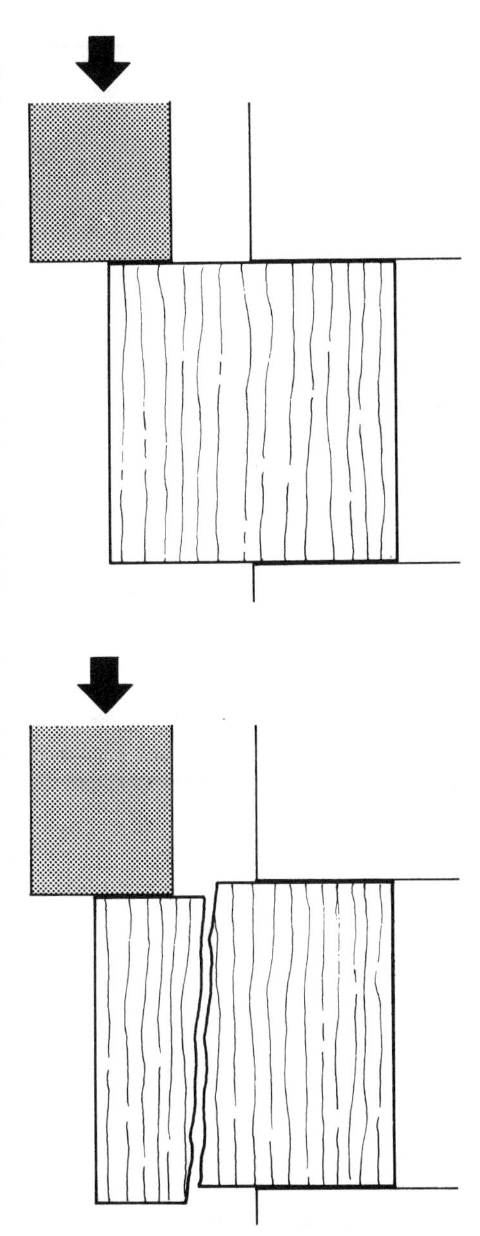

Fig. 48 *Shear stress testing.*

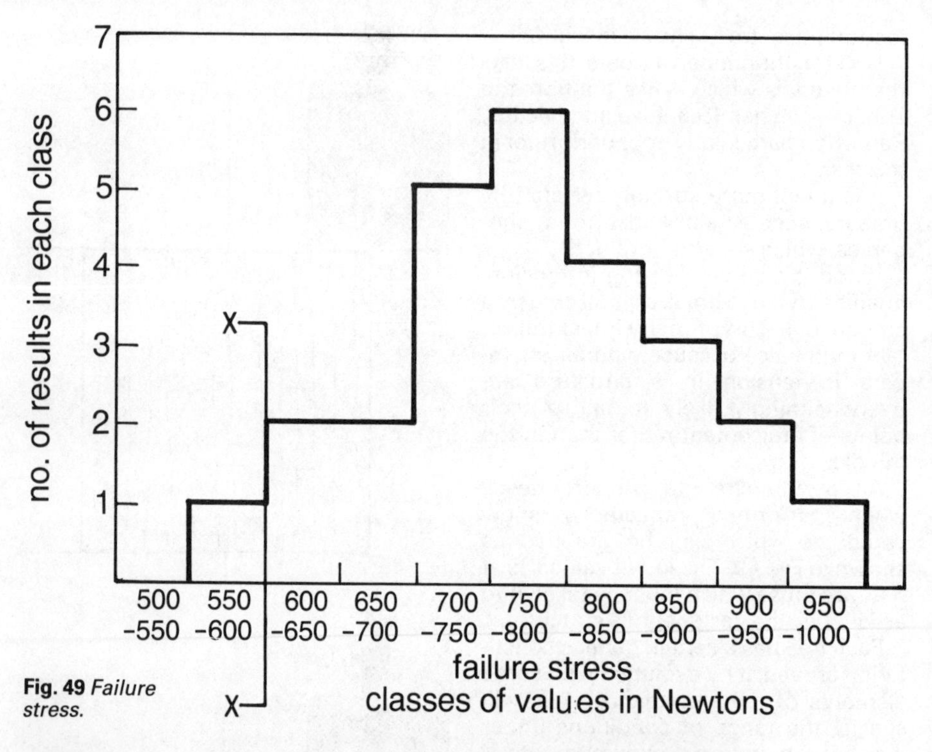

Fig. 49 *Failure stress.*

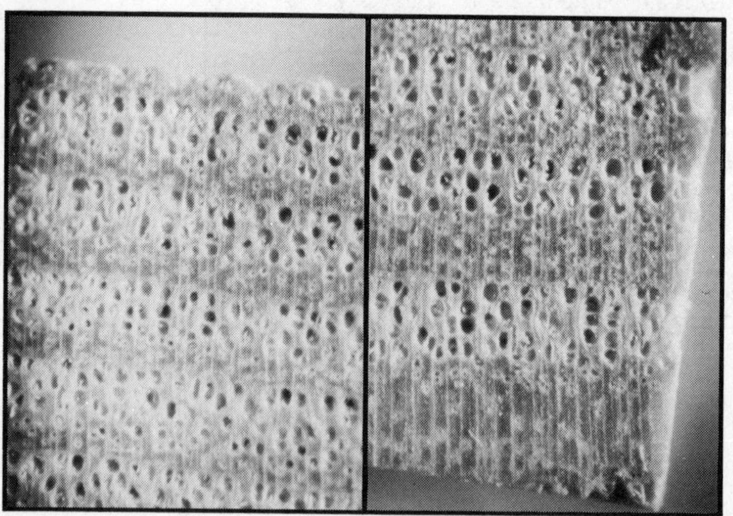

Fig. 50 *Ash slow grown and moderately fast grown. These two specimens averaged 11 and 18 rings per inch.*

per inch. Musical instrument manufacturers are generally only interested in spruce near the higher figure.

Hardwoods generally work in reverse to this principle. Fast growth tends to emphasise the latewood with more fibres, so many hardwoods are stronger when grown rapidly. This is particularly true of ring-porous woods like oak and ash. The ring of vessels in the earlywood is produced regardless. In very slow growth, it is almost the only xylem production giving a very low density wood of low strength. More favourable growing conditions lead to a thicker layer of libriform fibres in the latewood; the ring of vessels being about the same. Oak and ash are considered best at about 6–10 rings per inch.

Wood is designed to support the weight of the tree, and this causes greatest problems where the stem is leaning, as in sidebranches or wind leaning trunks. Hormonal mechanisms related to those that guide growth upward (see page 8) modify the structure of the wood to withstand this sidestress. Again hardwoods and softwoods approach this problem from opposite directions. 'Reaction wood' is produced but takes two forms.

Softwoods produce extra growth on the lower or compression side of a branch and this is called 'compression wood'. This timber has the cellulose fibres differently arranged and it has extra lignin. It is stronger in compression but can be quite weak in tension, and it shrinks more appreciably along its length. This means that, if a board contains some compression wood, it will distort on drying and/or show splits across the compression part. Compression wood is often redder, denser and harder but more brittle. It does not work or finish well.

Hardwoods produce 'tension wood', on the upper section of a trunk grown under sidestress. It is lighter, more lustrous, higher in cellulose and lower in lignin. It is stronger in tension and weaker in compression than the normal timber. Like compression wood, it is harder and denser but more brittle. In most other respects, it is the opposite of compression wood but, unfortunately, it is no better as timber and the woodworker buying from a reputable stockist should not come across it. The enterprising woodworker trying to make use of larger sidebranches, perhaps from prunings, is likely to find it a problem.

CHAPTER 5

TEXTURE, GRAIN AND FIGURE

These three terms are often confused and wrongly used, but they are always interlinked.

The term 'figure' relates to any visible surface feature which relieves the monotony of a cut surface. Timbers such as hornbeam and willow among temperate hardwoods, and perhaps jelutong from the tropics, often carry very little figure and appear rather 'boring'. Nonetheless, all of these timbers have a texture and a grain.

'Texture' is an explanation of the sizes of the xylem element holes best seen in the endgrain. Texture descriptions should carry two pieces of information – the size of the holes and the regularity of their spacing. Density and hardness are often quoted alongside texture, but texture does not essentially involve them. A timber may be fine or coarse textured, and even or uneven textured. Lacking vessels, most softwoods are described as fine textured, but where early and latewood differ in wall thickness and therefore density, they are of uneven texture. So pitch pine and Douglas fir are fine but unevenly textured woods. Yellow pine and yew are equally fine but evenly textured. Yew is relatively hard while yellow pine is not, showing that this feature is independent.

Hardwoods may be fine and even textured as, for example, willow or beech. They may be coarse but even textured as with many tropical timbers such as iroko. Most markedly ring-porous timbers would be regarded as

Fig. 51(a) *Pitch pine.*

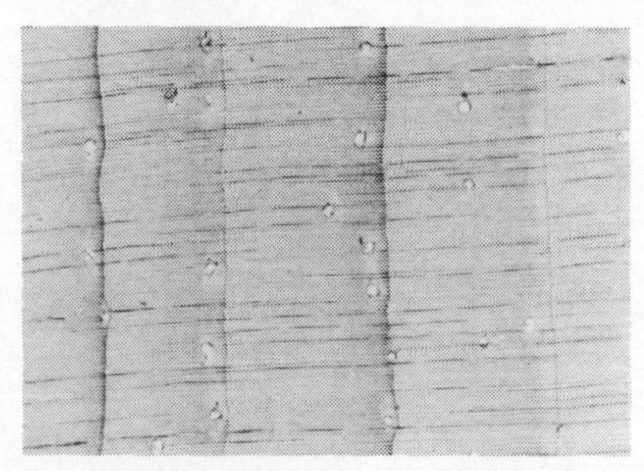

Fig. 51(b) *Yellow pine.*

coarse and uneven textured. These may be mainly temperate such as oak, ash and elm but would include teak. Even textured timber can be relatively lacking in figure but very useful for certain applications. So the softer even textured woods are favoured for carving, e.g. lime, and beginner's joinery, e.g. jelutong.

Uneven texture may itself create figure. For example, the principal small-scale figuring in ash is due to its obviously ring-porous nature. The larger scale figure of some softwoods, most obvious in Douglas fir, is due to the uneveness – the difference between early and latewood in colour. Where figure is the result of texture, in this way it is usually most elaborately shown on tangentially cut surfaces.

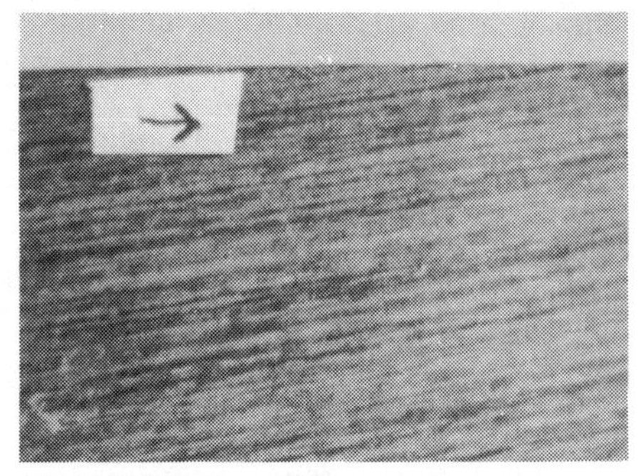

Fig. 52 *'With the grain'.*

The 'grain' of the wood describes the path of the axial water conducting fibres. These ought, perhaps, to run straight and parallel to the axis in perfectly cylindrical rows. In practice, this is not the case. Cutting at the conversion stage is

Fig. 53 *Lustre effects of grain direction.*

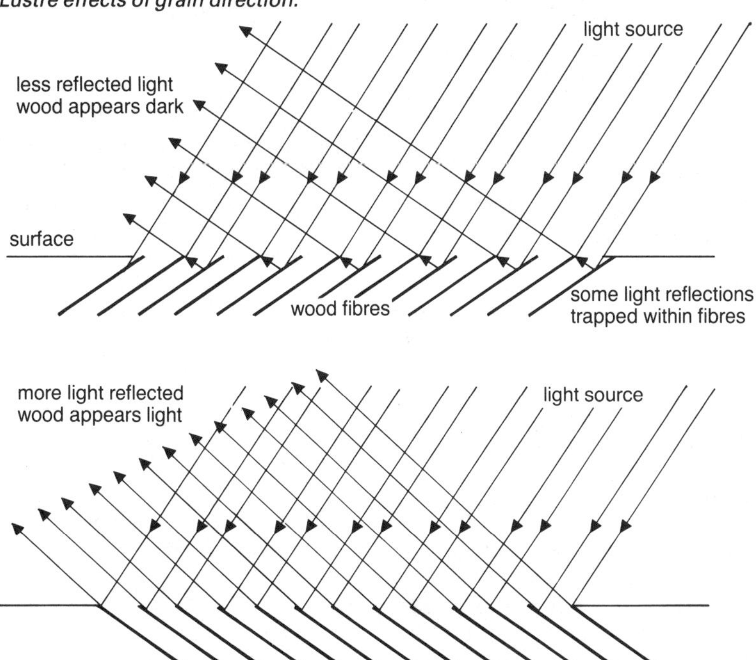

usually done very nearly parallel to the central axis, but the pieces (unlike those converted by splitting) often have grain which is not parallel to an edge (see visual grading Chapter Three).

In planing timber, as well as other operations, the angle between the grain and the timber edge has to be noted. To plane 'against the grain' is to invite the timber to try to split down into the surface which gives a very uneven finish. Planing 'with the grain' should ensure clean cutting of the fibres.

Woods which reflect light well from smooth surfaces are said to be 'lustrous'. The amount of light reflected depends on direction of lighting and grain (see Fig. 53). This principle explains so many of the fancy figures which can be found in woods where the grain is, in one way or another, not straight and the direction of cut reveals different grain angles on the same surface. In Chapter Three spiral grain was explained and shown. Many timbers have spiral grain but the direction of the spiral may change on a regular basis. The direction of cell orientation of the vascular cambium may change from what could be called an S spiral to a Z spiral in a few years, passing briefly through truly axial on the way. This changing spiral gives what is called 'interlocked grain'. It can make a timber very difficult to split and explains the use of elm for Windsor chair seats, for example. If this timber is radially cut, there will be strips with the grain at a positive angle to the surface (i.e. with the grain) alongside strips with a negative angle (against the grain). This feature is seen in most mahoganies (see Chapter Ten) and explains the general difficulty in planing them. It is seen most clearly in sapele, when radially cut, and is known as 'stripe figure'. The angle of incidence of the light causes the different grain angles to appear as light and dark stripes. Rotation of the piece through 180 degrees changes the light to dark and vice versa. Stripe figure veneers must be treated intelligently in some applications, particularly marquetry, if they are not laid in the angle of incidence of light that they are to be viewed in.

Fig. 54 *Stripe figure – African walnut.*

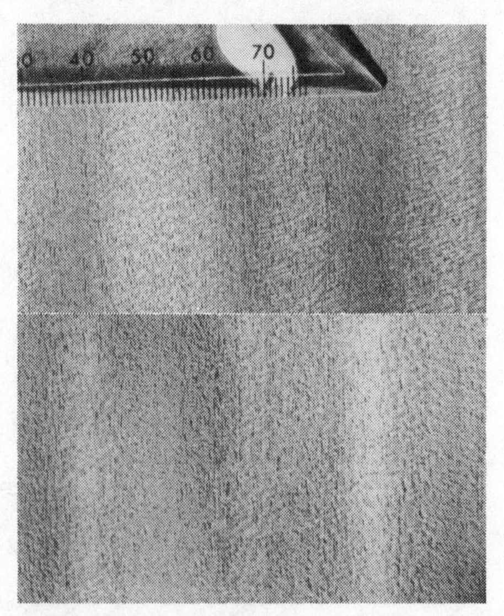

Fig. 55 *Striped grain in sapele with the lighting direction changed through 180°.*

There are many more complex patterns in which the grain to surface angle may vary. Instead of running obliquely, the xylem elements may follow a wavy path upward so that if we follow a line of elements it may be an S spiral at one point and a Z spiral a centimetre above and below. This wood would cleave flat tangentially but a radial cleavage would be corrugated. A flat radial cut surface will show alternate transverse stripes of light and dark lustre. This is most common in mahoganies and maples. So prized is this figure from the lower part of a maple trunk for violin backs that the pattern is called 'fiddleback'. Veneer can be obtained in which consecutive leaves, opened book fashion, present an almost perfect mirror image.

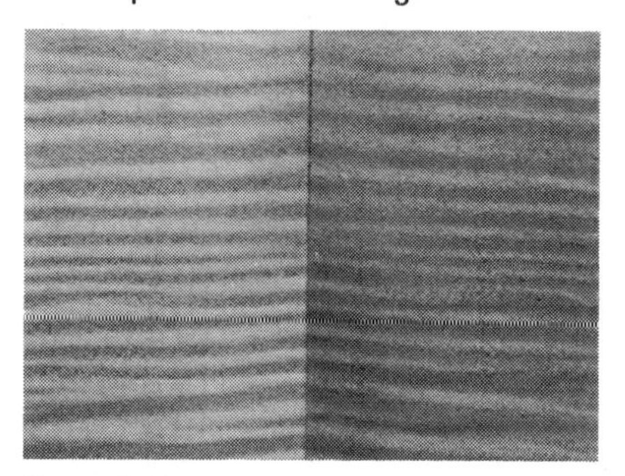

Fig. 56 *Fiddleback figure in two consecutive leaves of mahogany veneer.*

This timber cut tangentially would not produce such an obvious figure. Tangentially wavy grain can produce an interesting, though small-scale, figure in some woods.

In other species the outer surface of the xylem, where the all important vascular cambium lies, may show other variations from a perfectly cylindrical surface. In maple, small depressions in the surface may persist for many years, giving a wood which has small circular

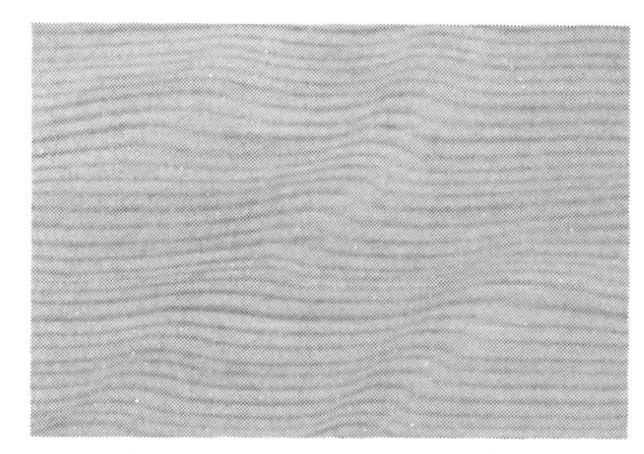

Fig. 57 *Wavy grain in Douglas fir. N.B. despite appearance this is a planed flat surface.*

Fig. 58 *Bird's eye maple.*

variations in grain/surface angle which, by lustre effects, creates 'Bird's Eye' figure on tangential surfaces. The same effect may occur on a larger scale, so that the larger, shallower depressions or elevations give a pattern called 'blister figure'. Larger and less obviously circular areas cause 'quilted figure'.

These variations from the cylindrical may be combined with tangential wanderings of grain direction to create a bewildering array of surface patterns. The combination of wavy grain and quilted figure gives what is termed 'roe figure'. The patterns of 'beeswing figure', as seen in East African satinwood, and the 'sunburst' figure, rarely seen in

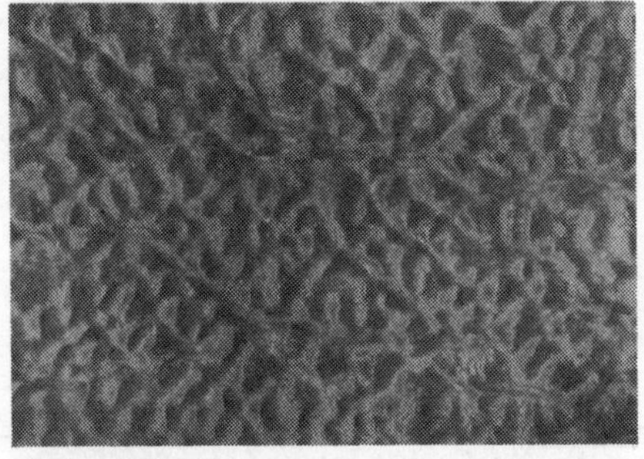

Fig. 59 *(above) East African satinwood beeswing figure.*

Fig. 60 *(below) Sunburst figured mahogany.*

mahoganies. I recommend the interested reader to find and study as they defy my powers of written explanation.

There are further complexities to figure in that there are at least two other major components which contribute to it. These are the radial component of the wood and the distribution of pigment, if any, in the heartwood.

In many timbers the radial system can be quite extensive but small, as in ash, or even quite complex as in hornbeam (see p 12), but not contribute to figure due to its lack of colour variation from the axial system. In other timbers, the rays may be quite well-coloured but too small to contribute to figure, at least at a furniture scale of finished item. Such tiny rays may be more significant on small or turned items.

Flat surfaces marked with growth rings and rays can be puzzling. It is often not clear in which direction these two sets of patterns depart beneath the surface. An understanding of such timbers can be greatly enhanced by the relatively elementary exercise of turning an egg shape from a piece of 50×50mm cross section. The result is a more instantly intelligible three-dimensional structure. It is an exercise I recommend to the prospective user of an unaccustomed timber. This will show the extent of the radial system figure. Clearly the oak and the Australian silky oak (*Grevillea sp*) are the prime examples of extensive radial system figuring. The tangential surface shows ray lines of no great interest. It is the radial surface of these timbers which show lustrous large expanses of ray tissue known as 'silver grain'. The perfectly radial surface would show large flat sheets and is seldom achieved. The almost radial gives a great variety of wandering lustrous cross streaks. This radial figure is the reason behind the special methods used for converting oak and is covered in Chapter Three.

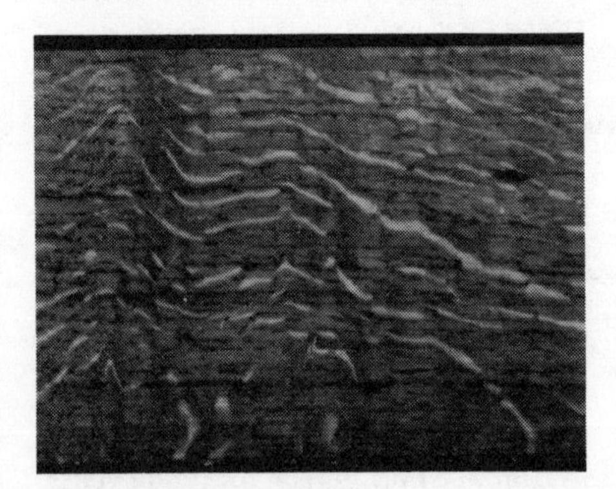

Fig. 61 *Silver grain in oak.*

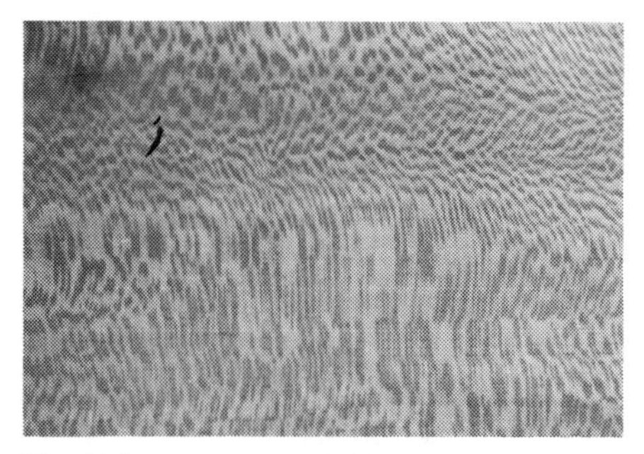

Fig. 62 *Lacewood – a highly developed radial system figuring.*

Other timbers where the ray system contributes to figure include beech and plane (lacewood). The name lacewood comes from the figure produced by the tightly regular dark and lustrous rays on radially cut surfaces. Smaller rays found in meranti and lauan can give very attractive patterns, but are seen to best advantage on small objects viewed more closely.

Pigment variations of the heartwood add another dimension to figure. Any specimen which includes pigmented heartwood and paler sapwood will present a striking contrast. Heartwood may be strikingly pigmented but, if evenly distributed, this can hardly be called figure, e.g. purpleheart. It can be distinctly unevenly distributed, as in zebrano, or less distinctly, as in temperate species of walnut. All have their own distinctive and attractive figures.

The figure that the worker in wood reveals and manipulates is a combina-

Fig. 63 *Heartwood and sapwood contrast – pau rosa.*

Fig. 64(a) *Zebrano – irregular pigment distribution.*

Fig. 64(b) *Walnut.*

tion therefore of texture, grain direction in two planes and variations in extent of growth rings and radial systems, knots and pigment impregnation.

The central portion of the newly-grown plant stem may not contain any lignin but may, as in herbaceous plants, be supported by the pressure of water within parenchyma cells. These form a 'pith' in the centre of many woody stems, made of soft tissue darker or lighter than the wood. It is of greatest extent in elder although this has no timber application. It is often seen in pine, and whether it is a figure feature or a defect may be left up to the user. It is a line of darker brown crumbly-looking tissue and is usually surrounded by a regular series of tiny knots which appear as dark dots. This is a feature of the early growth of many conifers. The leaves grow in twos or fives, depending on species, on tiny sidebranches which have their own xylem supply. Since these clothe the stem for two to three years there will be these knots in the first two to three growth rings.

Lines of pith-like tissue may also be created in some hardwoods in the burrows made by some tiny fly larvae. They are seen as short dark brown lines of indefinite direction. They can be found in maple and in alder but reach their greatest concentration in birch. This is called masur birch.

When a tree starts as a sapling, every leaf on the initial vertical stem forms a potential bud position. These buds may grow out into sidebranches and, eventually, knots. In some circumstances, the bud may fail to grow properly into a sidebranch. It may be damaged by herbivores or parasitic insects, or even the abrasion of passing animals. If the bud grows into a very short length of sidebranch, this too will have leaves and subsequently more bud positions. Alternatively the tissue damage may cause a

Fig. 65 *(below) Young pine trunk with leaves and (right) pine – pith and young pin knots.*

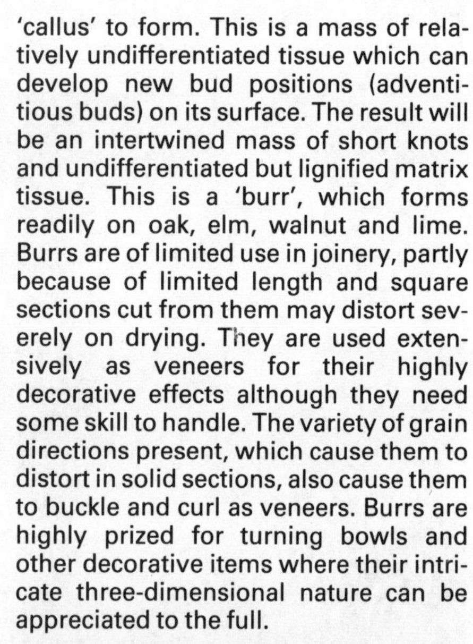

'callus' to form. This is a mass of relatively undifferentiated tissue which can develop new bud positions (adventitious buds) on its surface. The result will be an intertwined mass of short knots and undifferentiated but lignified matrix tissue. This is a 'burr', which forms readily on oak, elm, walnut and lime. Burrs are of limited use in joinery, partly because of limited length and square sections cut from them may distort severely on drying. They are used extensively as veneers for their highly decorative effects although they need some skill to handle. The variety of grain directions present, which cause them to distort in solid sections, also cause them to buckle and curl as veneers. Burrs are highly prized for turning bowls and other decorative items where their intricate three-dimensional nature can be appreciated to the full.

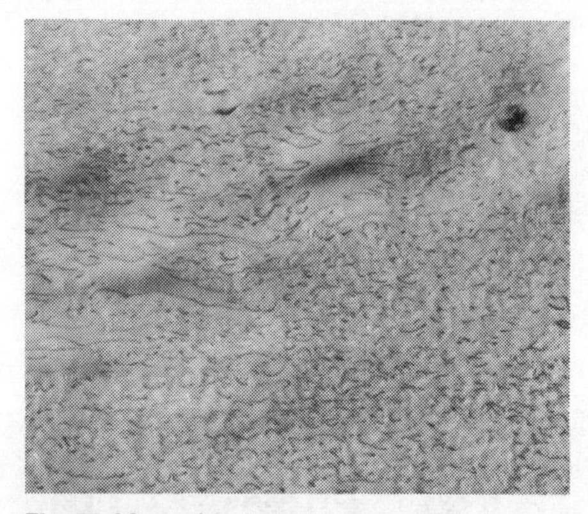

Fig. 66 *Masur birch.*

Fig. 67 *(below left) Burrs at the conversion stage. (below right) Burr figure – walnut. (opposite page) Burrs on a trunk.*

CHAPTER 6

OTHER CHEMICALS IN WOOD

In addition to cellulose and lignin there are a wide variety of other chemicals synthesised by the living parts of the trunk which are responsible for many of the properties of different timbers. These include those found in the heartwood which are responsible for its greater durability.

These chemicals have been termed 'extractives' because many of them can be extracted in organic solvents. If you have wood waste of some coloured or oily exotic timber it is an interesting exercise to soak fragments in alcohol for a couple of days and then allow most of the solvent to evaporate. Some interesting and surprising samples result. Try it on padauk or purpleheart or teak.

Some of these 'extractives' can be removed from the timber in simple solution while others cannot.

They have a variety of technical names which can be very confusing but which do actually fall into definable groups that show interesting interrelationships, especially to those conversant with, or at least not frightened by, structural organic formulae. We find resins, gums, oils, waxes, tannins, alkaloids and anthocyanins listed among wood's organic extractives while silica, lime and (technically incorrectly?) oxalates listed as minerals included in timbers but not generally extractable by solvents. Oxalates, notwithstanding their crystalline nature and calcium content, are organic since the oxalate part is so intimately based on carbon and the myriad ways it can combine together.

The commonest extraneous chemicals are probably the resins and gums, but there is some confusion of terms here. Gums is the term often given to soft or sticky substances in hardwoods, resins being reserved for those in softwoods. While there are distinct differences, they are not perfectly served by these terms. The term resin really means a substance containing a solvent which will not tend to crystallize when that solvent evaporates. Salt and sugar solutions yield crystals on drying because their molecules are the same size and shape and settle into regular arrangements. All the organic extractives are mixtures of chemicals so diverse that they cannot form crystals and therefore they are all technically resins.

The gums produced in hardwoods are mainly relatives of the cell wall materials themselves. They may be sparingly soluble in water, especially if hot, but tend to be insoluble in organic solvents. A very simple 'gum' extracted from

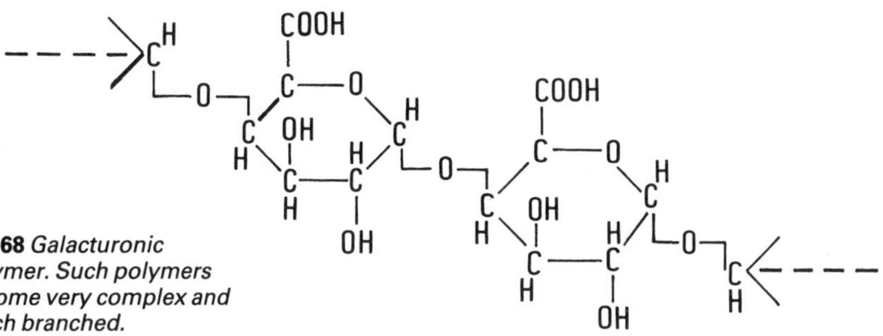

Fig. 68 *Galacturonic polymer. Such polymers become very complex and much branched.*

plant tissue by boiling water is the pectin formed in jam making. This is extracted by prolonged boiling from the middle lamella which adheres adjacent cells together in all plants. Gums, related to this pectin and to hemicellulose, are mixtures of glucuronic and galacturonic polymers along with short chain glucose polymers related to starch and/or cellulose and also polymers of less well-known sugars, such as xylose and mannose. Their insolubility can cause problems if organic based stains are used. South American cedar (*Cedrela fissilis* – a hardwood) is noted as finishing unevenly with oil based stains as the surface refuses to wet evenly, therefore water based stains are used. Agba is a timber which may produce so much gum that boards can actually stick together if stacked for long periods without wooden strips to separate them.

The substances so closely associated with some softwoods are called resins. They are better described, for reasons given above, as oleo-resins. They are mixtures of a wide range of compounds, most of them chemically classifiable as terpenes. These are alcohol and ketone derivatives of benzene and their polymers. Along with oleo-resins, the terpenes include, or are structurally related to, many of the aromatic plant oils like camphor, menthol, menthone (peppermint oil), citronollel (lemon oil) and geraniol (a flower scent) so their distribution in plants goes well beyond wood.

A natural oleo-resin can be distilled and separated into a volatile fraction which forms turpentine, and a solid fraction termed rosin. The precise temperature of the distillation will determine the nature of each fraction. Both fractions are still mixtures of a variety of compounds but typical examples can be seen in Fig. 69.

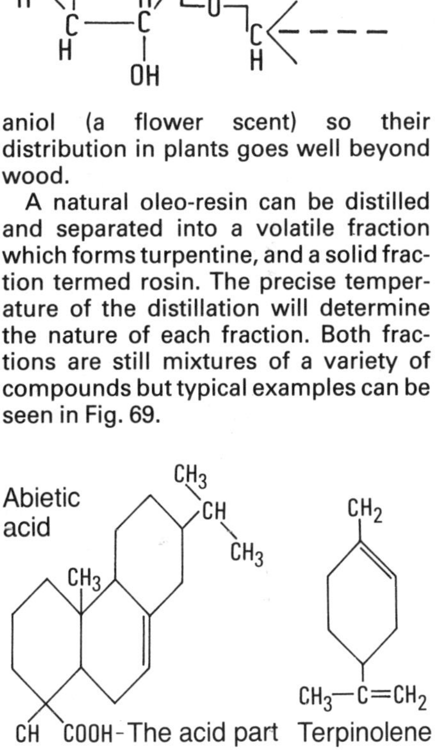

Abietic acid

COOH-The acid part

Terpinolene

Fig. 69 *Solid and liquid Terpenes.*

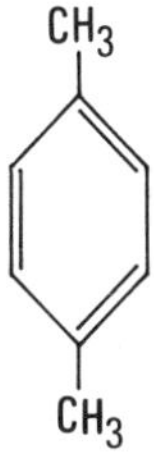

Fig. 70 *Xylene.*

Pure pine rosin is mainly abietic acid. Resin acids of this type may slowly oxidise in air. This is responsible for some of the complex aspects of the long-term seasoning of timber.

In view of the structure of terpinolene it is not surprising that the best resin solvents among the mineral oil fractions is xylene.

Oleo-resins are found in hardwoods often associated with gums. One difference is that the rosin fractions do not normally include the acid derivatives.

Other chemicals found in pine resin include the more complex ring structured pinene in the turpentine fraction and pinosylvin (a stilbene) in the rosin fraction. Pinosylvin has been shown to be partly responsible for the greater durability of the heartwood in pine.

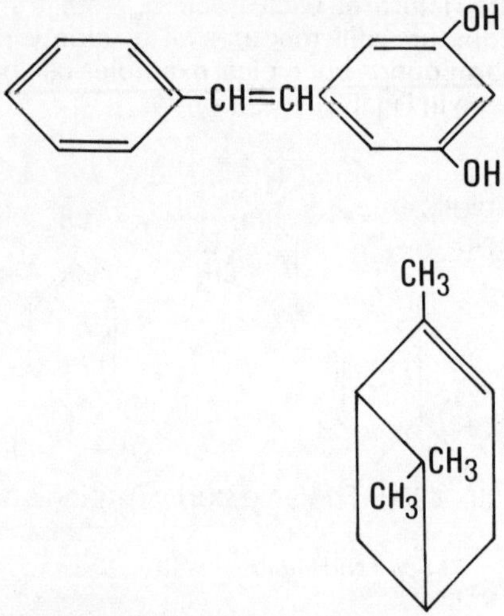

Fig. 71 *Pinosylvin – a stilbene. Pinene – a terpene.*

In Western red cedar (*Thuja sp.*) there is an unusual seven-membered ring called thujaplicin (a tropolone) responsible for much of its considerable heartwood durability.

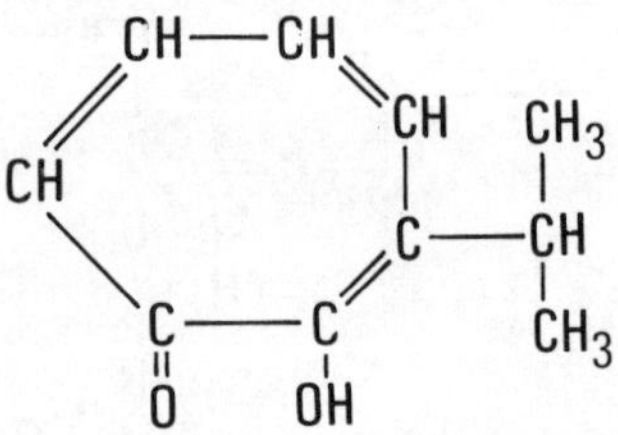

Fig. 72 *Thujaplicin – a tropolone.*

The oleo-resins, along with other terpenes, can be seen to be synthesised from a basic monomer unit – isoprene. If we look at the structure of pigments in the green parts of plants such as carotene we also find the isoprene basic unit. (Carotene is responsible for some of the autumn colouration of leaves as the green chlorophyll breaks down.).

Latex is present in some tree trunks, most notably the rubbertree – *Hevea braziliensis*, but also in jelutong. Latex will exude from cuts through the bark as a milky emulsion containing proteins, sugars and a wide range of less definable compounds. This is subjected to various treatments including boiling water which removes the sugars and rolled out into a raw material known as caoutchouc (pronounced cow-chook). This is sent to be vulcanised as the raw material of the very large rubber industry. If it is heated, however, it breaks

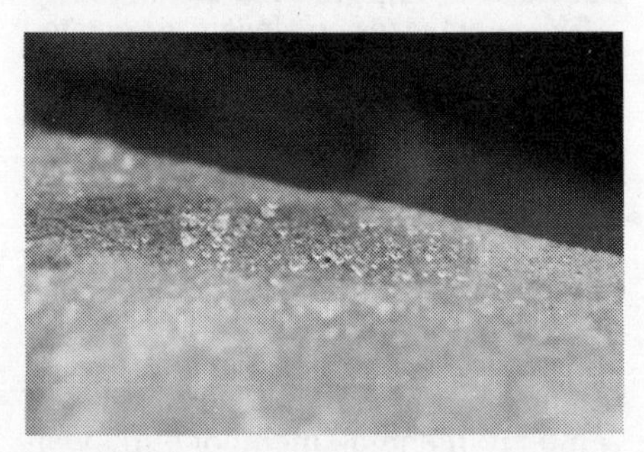

Fig. 73 *Gum droplets exuding from keruing.*

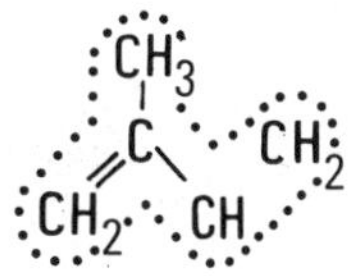

Isoprene unit

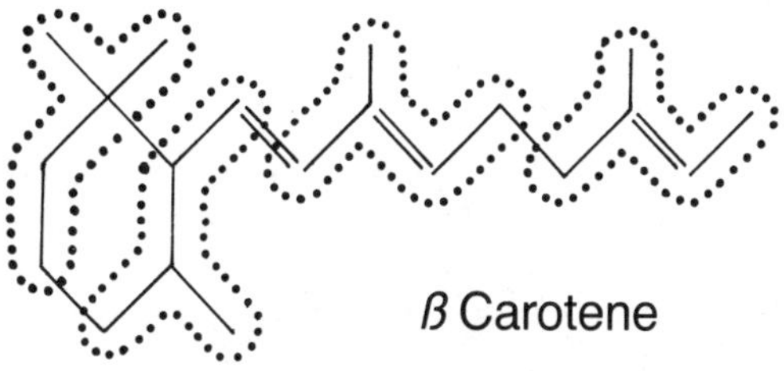

β Carotene

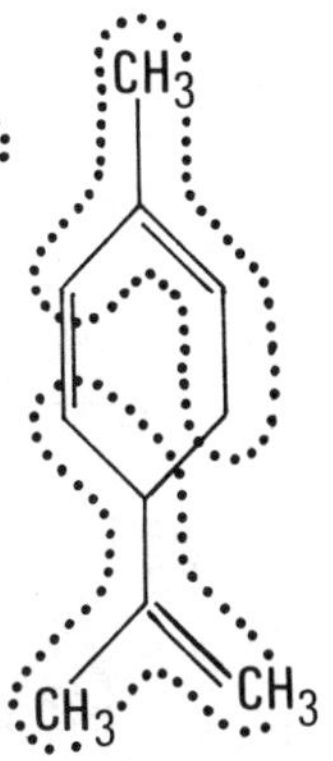

terpinolene

Fig. 74 *Isoprene unit, β carotene, terpinolene.*

down to give a proportion of isoprene. It bears some chemical relationship to the oleo-resins therefore despite its very different appearance.

Another group of compounds associated with durability properties in some timbers are the tannins. These are also complex mixtures but again some simple examples can be given. (See Fig. 75).

You can draw out for yourself formulae which are intermediate in size between these two and they probably exist in tannins – so diverse are the mixtures. These molecules can then polymerise! Tannins are often found in the bark and the leaves as well as the wood. They are widely used to form permanent and toxic cross linkages with proteins in animal skins; the basis of tanning leather. This precipitation may be the key to their chemical attack on insects and fungi. Since both produce enzyme proteins to digest the wood structure, precipitation of these enzymes would chemically inhibit the digestive attack of these pests on timber.

Tannins are usually colourless, but they form coloured compounds with some other materials, notably iron. Hence the incompatibility of oak with iron nails and the corrosive effects of oak left in contact with steel tools. Oak can be turned black by soaking in a soluble iron salt. Ammonia will also darken oak by affecting tannins. The grey shades of harewood veneers produced from sycamore soaked in ferrous sulphate are due to the lesser concentrations of tannin in this timber.

Some of the pigments associated with timbers fall into the category of anthocyanins. These are responsible for so many of the blue/purple/red colours of flowers and berries and the more delicate, though sometimes light fugitive colours of woods like plum.

Anthocyanins can be separated into one molecule of a sugar, often glucose and an anthocyanidin. Study of the for-

Fig. 75 *Gallic acid, catechin, two tannins.*

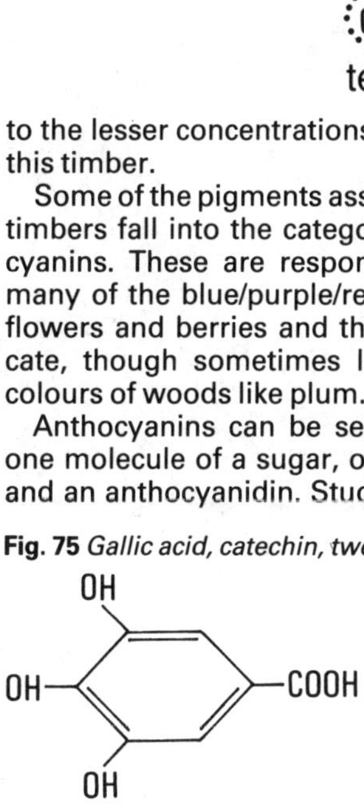

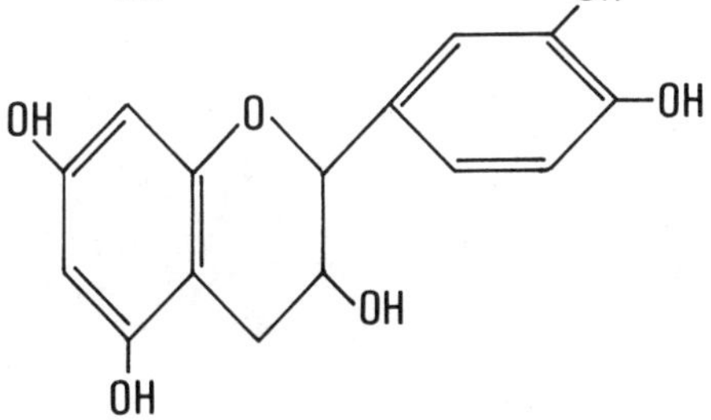

Fig. 76 *Latex treatment plant. Latex is converted to caoutchouc.* (photo courtesy Malaysian Rubber Products Research Association).

mula of an anthocyanidin shows that it is almost identical to a formula given above for a tannin. In terms of molecular structure and the way they are formed, tannins and anthocyanins are almost the same.

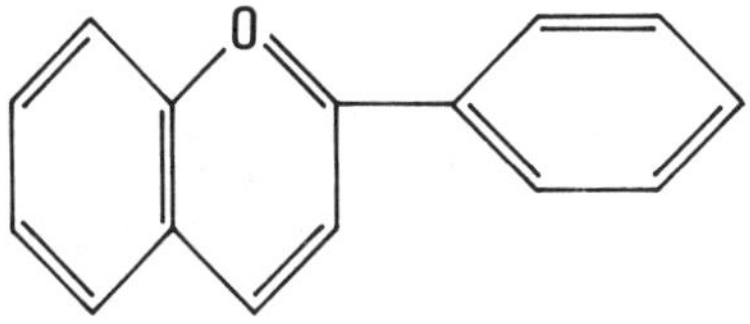

Fig. 77 *Flavylium – an anthocyanidin.*

The relationship between tannins and various pigments can cause chemical staining to be a problem with some types of glue and/or finishing materials. Some of the shades of red found in some heartwoods are the result of chemicals called phlobaphenes – insoluble tannin derivatives. It is interesting to note that apart from iron staining already mentioned, the commonest staining problem with oak is a pink colouration. This may result from the use of urea; formaldehyde glues on oak or sycamore. It can also result from the use of 2-part finishes with acid; alcohol catalyst hardeners.

Another tannin which is a pigment is ellagic acid which is the cause of the characteristic yellow/brown colour of idigbo.

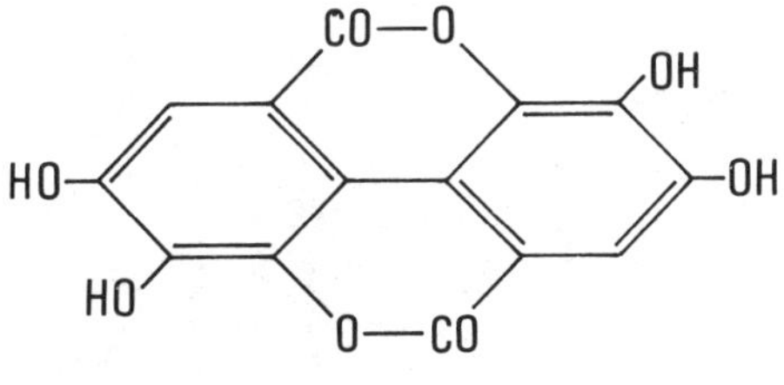

Fig. 78 *Ellagic acid – one of the pigments in Idigbo (a tannin).*

Alkaloids are even more diverse. They all contain nitrogen often in an otherwise carbon ring. There is no basic or typical formula. The list of better known alkaloids includes atropine, strychnine, nicotine and cocaine so clearly a degree of animal toxicity is a common feature. This undoubtedly gives them a protective role in the wood as well as in the leaves.

Many of them derive from well known cellular synthesis mechanism. Some are derived from the amino acid (protein monomer) tryptophan. The hormone auxin (see page 8) is also a tryptophan derivative. Others come from the constituents of the hereditary material – D.N.A.

Timbers more heavily impregnated with alkaloids may cause skin irritation on handling and various undesirable symptoms if dust is inhaled. Mansonia and makore are the most notorious of these but iroko and teak also cause some problems.

While the tannins and alkaloids are generally distributed in the wood, bark and leaves, the gums, resins and latexes are associated with distinct channels in the wood. The resins are secreted by parenchyma cells and may remain confined to these cells as in sequoia or may be pushed into adjacent tracheids as in parana. They may come to occupy passages between cells called resin ducts or canals. In pines, larches, spruces and Douglas fir these run both axially and radially. These ducts are called shizogenous (shizo – splitting) where they are caused by cells parting company and lysigenous – (lyso – dissolving) where cell walls disintegrate to form them. In addition, any split or shake which forms, or weak area between cells, is likely to be filled with resin, termed traumatic (trauma – damage) resin ducts. These are often referred to as pitch pockets and

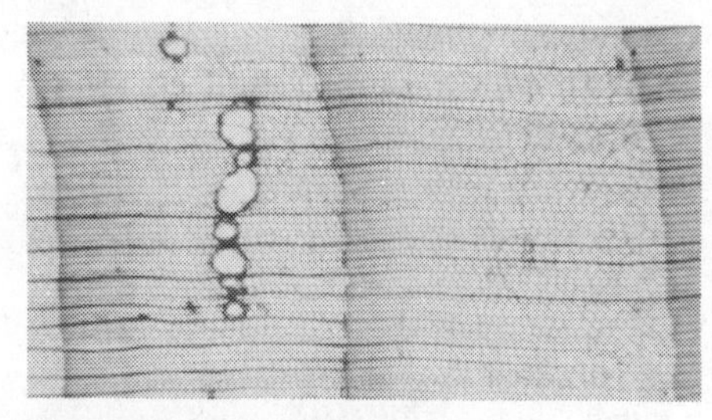

Fig. 79 *Resin ducts in pine.*

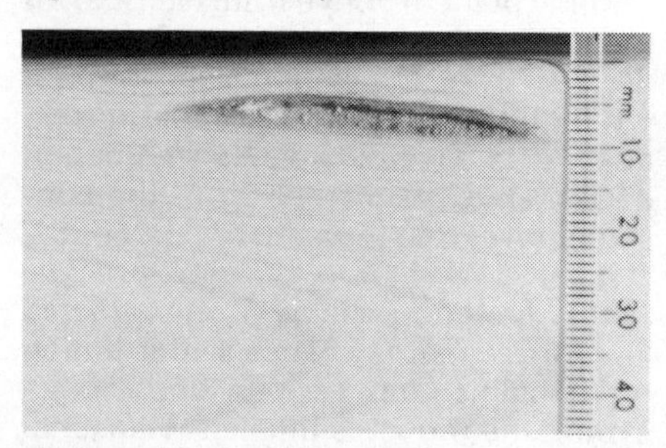

Fig. 80 *Pitch pocket – Scots pine.*

may be very large. Traumatic filling of any damaged area is connected with the function of resins in physically gumming up boring insects in the living tree. The effectiveness of this may be judged by the number of good insect fossils found in fossilised oleo-resin exudates – amber.

Gum ducts may also be shizogenous, lysigenous or traumatic. Some woods have axial ducts – African walnut, some have only radial ducts – Goncalo alves. The dipterocarp group including keruing and all the meranti/lauan timbers have both.

Latex occurs mostly in large, axially elongated and enlarged cells of parenchyma origin or in larger radial canals as seen in jelutong. Latex canals of this sort can be mistaken for insect burrows in some timbers.

The chemicals termed minerals cannot normally be extracted from timber due to their relative insolubility. One of these is silica. Silica may form tiny crystals invisibly embedded in the cell walls in some timbers or larger crystals in parenchyma cells. Since silica is, to all intents and purposes, sand, it is not surprising that such timbers have a marked blunting effect on tools. Australian turpentine wood and Queensland walnut are the often quoted though uncommon examples. Teak and iroko also show this as well as keruing and makore.

Calcium salts may be found as crystalline lumps visible in the parenchyma cells. These may be calcium carbonate (limestone) and/or calcium phosphate

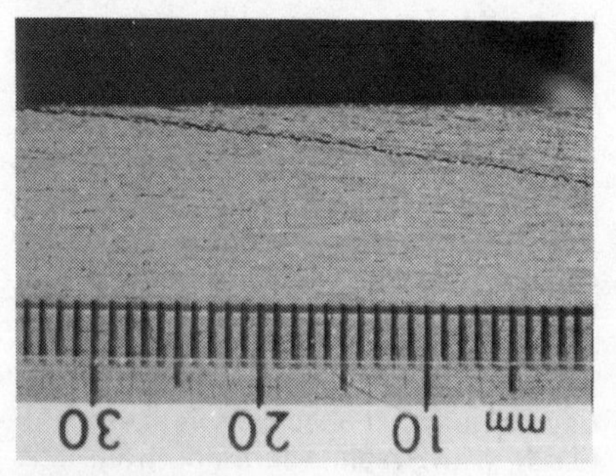

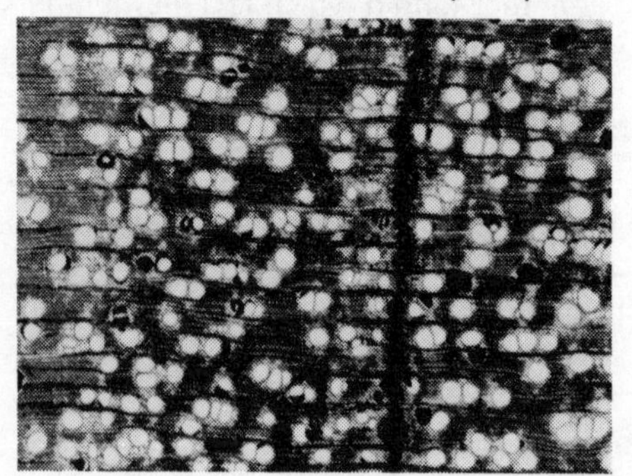

Fig. 81(a) *Gum vein – African walnut.*
Fig. 81(b) *The same gum vein in cross section (arrowed).*

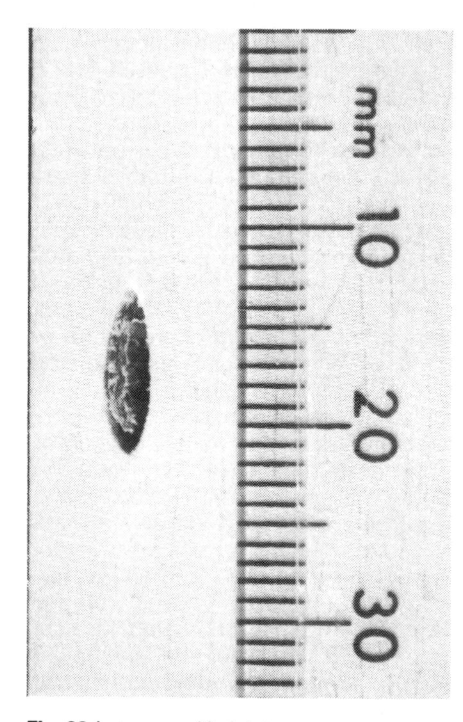

Fig. 82 *Latex canal in jelutong.*

(apatite). Since these two are the main constituents of bone and tooth enamel, these too may be judged rather damaging to fine edged tools. This is combined with silica in teak and iroko. In iroko in particular, this material may fill internal splits in the trunk to give the appearance of veins and fillings of fine concrete.

Calcium oxalate, although partly an organic compound, behaves as a mineral in terms of being crystalline and insoluble. It forms crystalline lumps in parenchyma cells which may be partitioned with cross walls into compartments with one crystal in each. They are found in afrormosia and occasionally in the very limited parenchyma in abies spp firs. They are less hard and blunting, although in afrormosia some silica is also present.

It is possible that, like the resins, gums and alkaloids that a tree uses to protect itself, the minerals also have protective properties. Calcium oxalate is poisonous and the other minerals must also inhibit the burrowing of insects by blunting their tools. i.e. mandibles.

All of these additional chemicals are pressed into service as a defence against the fungi and insects which would attack the wood during the life of the tree. Although converted into usable forms, they are basically excretory products; the toxic wastes of the living outer parts of the tree trunk. They are conveyed into the centre which now only functions in support. It is the living parenchyma cells of the ray system which move these chemicals inward, modifying them en route. Once in the central area, these materials are dumped and heartwood is formed. The materials may be left impregnated into cell walls, or be accumulated by parenchyma cells which die, or they may be pushed out into the otherwise empty spaces in the xylem vessels. The way in which this is done is interesting and very significant to the properties of some timbers. During heartwood formation in many species, the living parenchyma cytoplasm will grow through a pit in the wall adjacent to a xylem vessel and fill the space with a balloon-like cytoplasmic outgrowth. Usually the nucleus of the parenchyma cell will also migrate into the xylem vessel. This entire growth then becomes packed with a mixture of the heartwood chemicals and dies. The structure is called a tylosis, (plural tyloses). Often it will completely block the vessel space. If a fungus-attacked timber specimen is sectioned and viewed under the microscope it may be seen that the growing fungus threads are considerably impeded by these toxic blockages. They also affect the flow of liquids through timber. Timbers with tyloses are always likely to be less susceptible to preservative impregnation (see Chapter Eight). The 'white oaks' – *Quercus robur* and *Q. petrea* are suitable for tight cooperage (waterproof barrels) while red oaks -*Q.rubra* etc. are too porous as they do not possess tyloses.

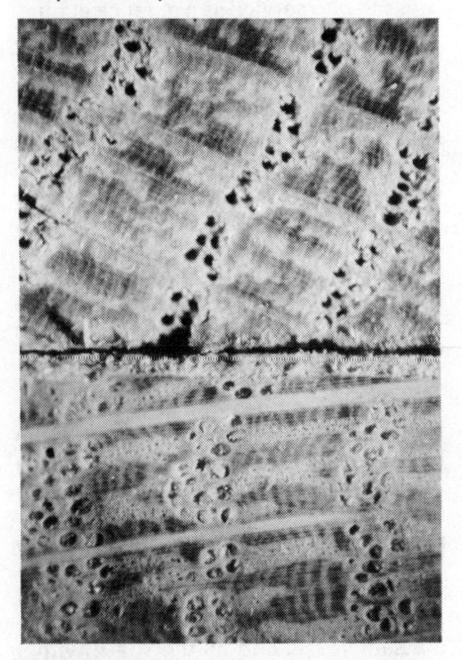

Fig. 83 *Red oak and white oak compared – tyloses show in white oak.*

In order to make the best use of a timber, its structure and its chemical nature need to be understood. The chemicals which are used to glue and/or finish a piece may chemically interact with materials in the wood. This has already been described for the tannin in oak. Other timbers contain chemicals which may be incompatible or cause staining. Teak is a timber noted for its oily nature. This oil may cause a lack of surface contact with water-based glues unless it is first removed from gluing surfaces with organic solvents. Teak also contains a quinone – tectoquinone – which may react preferentially with peroxide catalysts where these occur in glues or finishes such as catalysed polyester resin varnish. Similar problems may occur in rosewoods and cocobolo among others. Acid timbers may have similar effects on phenol and resorcinol glues if their water content is high. Oak, chestnut and idigbo can suffer these problems as well as yellow pine. Thorough seasoning should prevent this. Some timbers may be so water-absorbent that they withdraw the water from water-soluble glues before setting can occur, e.g. obeche. The opposite may occur with very dense timbers where the water cannot evaporate sufficiently. This is true of ekki, greenheart, ebony, some rosewoods and particularly lignum vitae where the problem is compounded by the waxy oleo-resin in this timber.

The most common type of finishing problem is that of painting ordinary oil based paints over resinous timbers such as some samples of pine. Since turpentine is both the paint solvent and the volatile fraction of the oleo-resin in

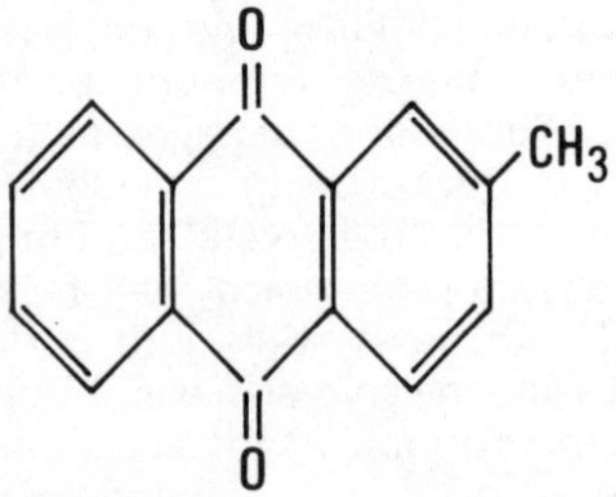

O

CH_3

O

Fig. 84 *Tectoquinone.*

the timber, paint may be slow to dry over resinous patches or knots. More seriously the resin, if warmed by the sun, may become more fluid and mobile and bleed through the paint, breaching its surface. Fortunately the solution is relatively simple and consists of covering all resinous areas in a layer of resin not soluble in turpentine. Shellac is used, known as 'knotting'.

CHAPTER 7

DRYING AND SEASONING

Freshly-felled timber is usually referred to as 'green'. In this situation, its sapwood is totally filled with water and its heartwood will contain, in addition to certain chemicals, some water and some air, or whatever gas mixture it might be.

This water exists in three forms:

(1) Free water in xylem members
(2) Cell sap and cytoplasmic water in parenchyma, (negligible in softwoods generally).
(3) Water bound between cellulose molecules.

Free water is the first to be removed and the main effect of its loss is a weight reduction (see ref teak p.38). The cytoplasmic water in the living cells adds to the food value and availability of the proteins, fats and carbohydrates in the sapwood and gives an added susceptibility to some pests of stored unseasoned hardwoods (see Chapter Eight). The cellulose bound water is between the cellulose molecules and to some extent holds them apart. Its removal, therefore, causes shrinkage. Since timber is, for many purposes, unusable until it has finished shrinking, these three forms of water must be removed. They are removed in the order given above, although with some overlap. This removal of water to give a stable timber is called seasoning, although other words may be used to indicate the way in which it was achieved (air-drying, kilning etc.).

Since timber will dry out to match the air around it, it follows that the eventual home of the timber needs to be known before it can be dried out to a level where it will neither shrink nor swell in this situation. Some of these are given in Fig. 85.

Water levels of timber quoted as percentages mean that percentage of the total weight which is water. This can be found by taking a sample of the timber large enough to be weighed accurately and, after weighing, put into an oven at minimum heat setting, preferably 100°C, until it stops losing weight.

$$\%\ \text{water} = \frac{\text{Weight loss on drying}}{\text{Final weight}} \times 100$$

A quicker method involves an electronic meter with two metal probes which drive into the timber like nails. This only measures the water level at the probes' depth and it can vary throughout the timber.

Water molecules move about with a speed and energy dependent upon tem-

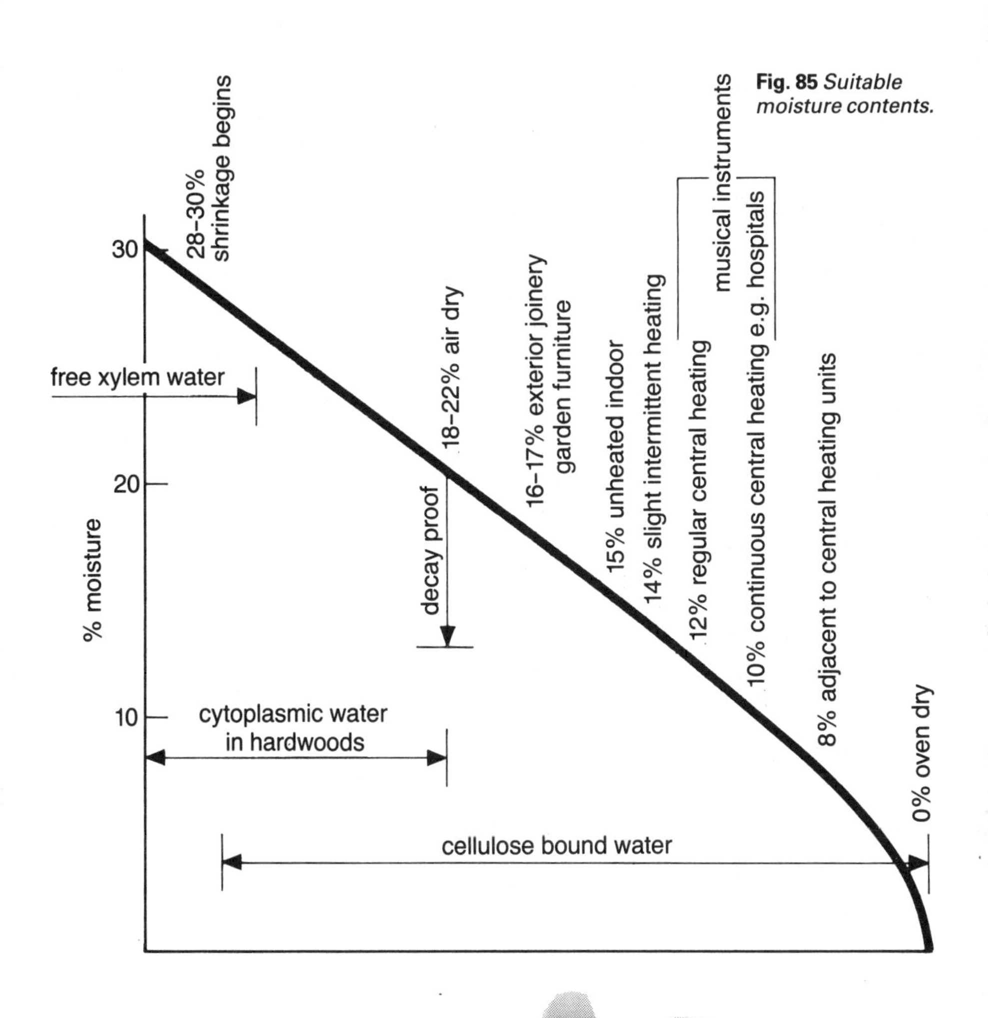

Fig. 85 *Suitable moisture contents.*

Fig. 86 *Moisture meter showing the two metal probe electrodes.*

perature. At a water/air surface, some water molecules may escape from the liquid as they attain the higher speed and energy necessary to become a water vapour molecule. In this situation, evaporation is occurring and obviously heating will accelerate this. If the water vapour molecules in air are losing energy, some of them will slow down and add themselves to the liquid water. This is condensation. The number and energy of the water molecules in the air and the liquid water will govern which process predominates. The drying effect of air is expressed as its 'relative humidity' [R.H.] This is a complex parameter since it is controlled by two simultaneous variables – the number of water molecules in the air and its temperature.

R.H. is expressed as:

$$\frac{\text{Amount of water in air}}{\text{Amount of water it could hold at that temperature}}$$

This can be measured with a wet and dry bulb thermometer but more usually an electronic hygrometer is used.

R.H. will change with temperature as well as moisture content. Air which is causing rapid evaporation from a surface can become a source of condensation simply by cooling it down. Similarly, an air water interface showing condensation at one temperature can switch to rapid evaporation with no other change than a rise in temperature. Still air may rapidly develop a high R.H. close to a water surface, slowing evaporation. Moving air, by removing this wet air boundary layer, speeds evaporation without change of temperature. Evaporation rates are, therefore, dependent on four factors; wet surface temperature, air temperature, air water vapour content and air speed. In the case of seasoning timber, the air water interface is somewhere within the timber itself. Initially, it is the surface of the timber but increasingly it is dispersed down into the complex wood structure.

Wood is designed to convey water and it will tend to move water vapour in the same direction as liquid water. This means that water vapour will leave the timber most rapidly and easily at the endgrain. Water vapour will move through timber tangentially, as the bordered pits in the tracheids were designed to allow. It will move radially much more slowly. This will occur through the rays as they dry and lose cytoplasmic contents but vapour passage through latewood in many timbers is very slow indeed.

The problem of drying timber efficiently is that the timber cannot naturally be dried evenly throughout its depth. The central portion will be the last to lose its water and shrink. The force with which this shrinkage occurs is considerable. If the outer portions shrink too much before the centre has started to shrink then splits can result, particularly in the endgrain. As the centre dries and shrinks, these splits may apparently close but this only conceals a lack of structural coherence; the sides of a split do not re-adhere as they close.

If the surface does not split it may

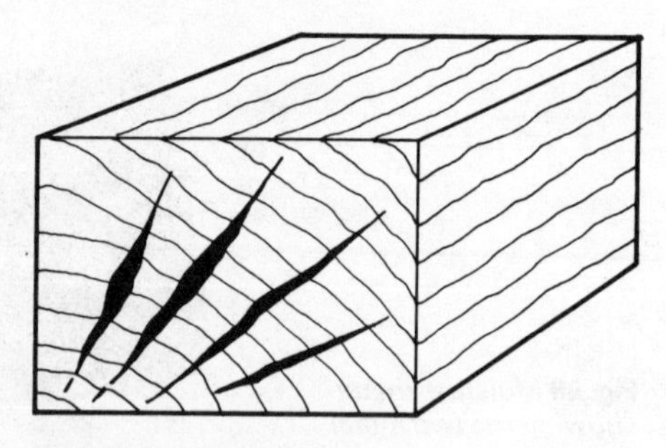

Fig. 87 *Honeycomb splits.*

Fig. 88
Seasoning timber.

remain stretched but harden. Seasoned timber is harder than green timber. If the surface hardens while stretched (is set in tension) the inner parts may dry more slowly and shrink more naturally, such that it becomes smaller than the exterior. Splits may develop internally (called 'honeycombing'). If these splits do not form, the timber may look quite normal but change shape alarmingly as soon as it is cut. Alternatively, the interior of the timber may not yet be fully shrunk and its moisture content may, to some extent, be sealed in by the hardened exterior. This phenomenon of premature seasoning of the exterior surfaces is known as 'case-hardening'. A rebate taken out of a case-hardened section will cause it to bow. Simply planing away one case-hardened face can have a similar effect.

Several methods are employed to reduce this problem of splitting and checking. The endgrain loses water most quickly and is the most likely part to split. This may waste a lot of timber if 30cm of the end of every board is unusable. One method of overcoming this is to cover the endgrain in melted paraffin wax. This solidifies to seal the endgrain forcing the water to depart sideways. In some cases, metal cleats can be employed to hold the endgrain from moving. Damp hessian has been used, hung over the endgrain to slow evaporation, although this would be rather a supervision-intensive method to use today. In practice high wastages are accepted as inevitable although, in view of the price of timber and concerns over its conservation, (see Chapter Nine) this is difficult to understand. Wax materials are less expensive than good timber.

A slow and even rate of drying is required to avoid these problems occurring. In years gone by, all timber was seasoned 'in stick'. A year for every inch of thickness of section cut was the rule of thumb. Logs were cut and stacked, with boards in sequence ('in boule') on a flat surface protected from rising ground moisture. They were separated by square section pieces of timber ('sticks'), such that the board faces were held apart by ½ – 1 inch and were then preferably covered from rain and direct sunlight but not from the wind. The main problem with this approach is the sheer variability of our climate. Throughout most of the winter months little drying would take place at low temperatures and high R.H. This could be used to some advantage to ensure a slow start to drying. In the warmer months, R.H. can be both dangerously low and extremely variable. Dry, still air would be likely to dry endgrain rapidly but leave the board faces with a layer of damp air immobile between them. Dry air (low R.H.) can have much less effect when it cools in the evening.

To understand the sheer unreliability of external air drying, we must look more closely at water levels in timber and its likely evaporation rates.

As water content falls to 28–30% shrinkage begins in most timbers. 28–30% is called 'fibre saturation point' and indicates that free water in the xylem elements is reaching zero. From this point down, it is bound water which is being removed and dimensions reduce with water loss. How much water evaporates depends on the air around the timber. An equilibrium can be set up between the water content of the timber and the R.H. of the air. This is called the 'equilibrium moisture content' of the timber. To dry the timber further, lower R.H. air is required. Higher R.H. air would increase the water content of the timber.

See Fig. 89 sample graph of air R.H. and E.M.C. for an average timber at 20°C.

Hot summer R.H. values can be as low as 25% in mid-afternoon but will probably be 70% again by evening, and through the night may easily reach 100% giving mists at dawn. The average R.H. may be difficult to decide upon, but it would appear that air-drying timber could be absorbing moisture almost as much as it is losing it. In a wet summer, the best R.H. may be no better than 75% and possibly 90% taken over 24 hrs. Under these conditions, it can be seen that there is no guarantee of timber ever being dried to the point of becoming fungus decay-proof, let alone useful for furniture. It is alarming to think that, in days gone by, ambient conditions air-drying was the only method available. Presumably more wastage was

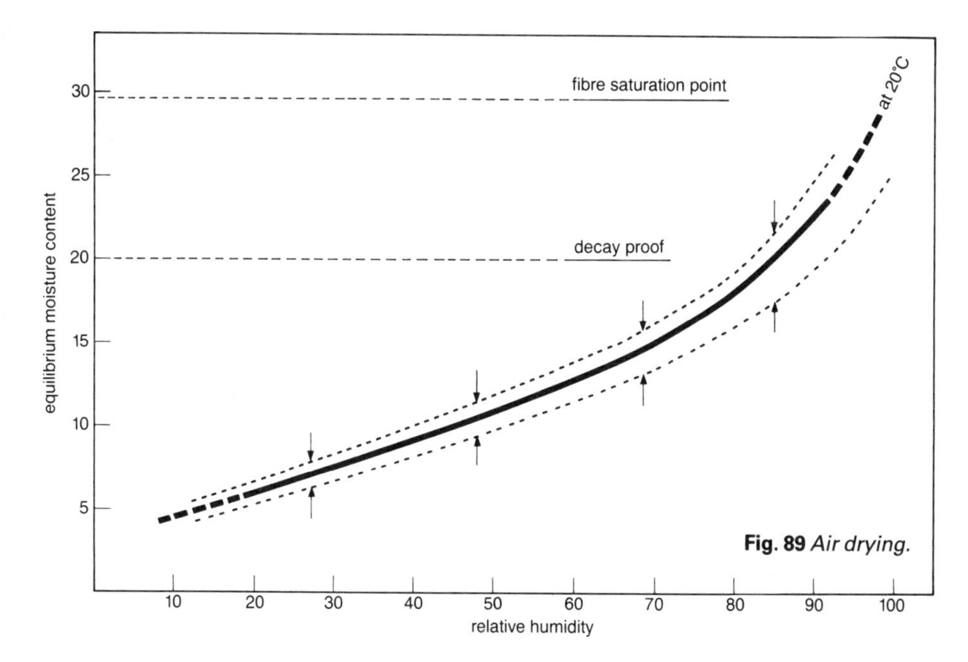

Fig. 89 *Air drying.*

accepted and, of course, the lack of central heating reduced the need for the 12% moisture content we look on today as standard.

Kilning is now the accepted method and is the only way timber can be brought down to moisture contents acceptable for modern indoor furniture.

A kiln is a closed chamber in which timber is stacked in a similar way to that explained for air-drying. The temperature, relative humidity and movement of air can all be controlled. This allows a kiln to dry timber at a controlled rate which should avoid surface and end-grain checks and case-hardening. In order to accelerate this drying, the temperature of the chamber is raised. This increases the mobility of water within the timber by increasing the movement of the molecules. Water will migrate towards the surface in response to a gradient of water content more rapidly at higher temperatures. In addition, the temperature affects the balance between E.M.C. and R.H. of air in a manner independent of its direct effect on R.H. (see Fig. 90). So, in a kiln it is possible, by raising the temperature, to draw out water from inside timber without simultaneously overdrying the surface. This is not to suggest that overdrying cannot occur. If the parameters are not correctly controlled, serious timber damage may result. High temperatures with R.H. too low can result in the kinds of damage already described. In addition, a state known as 'collapse' may occur when the cells have water withdrawn from them so quickly that they get partially sucked flat. This gives an almost shapeless board with a corrugated surface. The average woodworker is unlikely ever to see this as it should never reach reputable resale outlets. Provided the controls of a kiln are

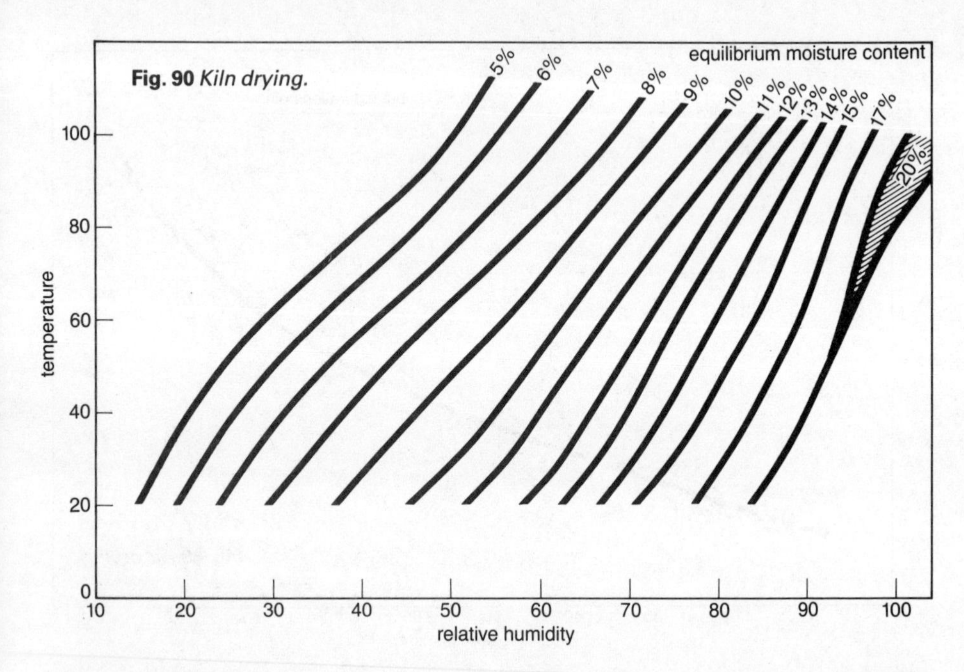

Fig. 90 *Kiln drying.*

correctly manipulated for the type of timber being dried, it is possible to bring timber to a reliable water content in a period measured in weeks rather than years.

The kiln is no longer a remote part of some timber warehouse but is increasingly becoming available to the woodworker who can obtain green timber. Modern small-scale units can be fitted to cabinets not beyond the size or complexity to be made and operated in the small/medium workshop. These can be made very energy -efficient by the use of a heater and dehumidifier. The dehumidifier is basically a refrigeration unit. Warmed air is passed over the timber and is then cooled, raising its R.H. to over 100% so water condenses and is removed as liquid. The condensing water gives up some heat energy, termed latent heat. The air, now dryer, takes up some of this latent heat and is further heated to be passed round the chamber again. The water in the timber leaves the insulated chamber as cold water and all heat is recycled. Some larger and older designs vented water as steam but this loses too much expensive heat energy.

The temperature in the chamber may be 35–75°C which greatly increases water mobility but it also increases the plasticity of the timber. As a result any inaccuracy in keeping sticks in vertical files or the chamber floor flat may result in a pile of boards all with the same wavy pattern. Kilning does not prevent shrinkage or the inevitable shape change due to radial/tangential shrinkage differences. If this causes timbers to move, those stacked above may set distorted. For this reason, weighting or even clamping of piles is recommended.

Control of the kiln settings is important but becomes less critical when the

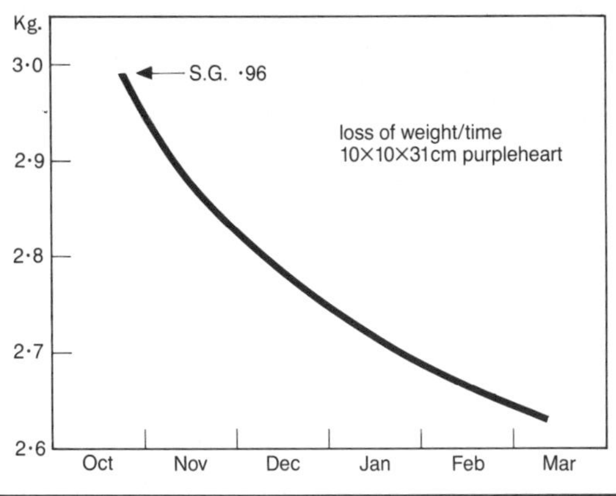

Fig. 91 *This 10 × 10 × 31cm block of purpleheart was bought by the author in October 1987. It was left in the corner of the lounge to equilibrate and weighed regularly. This might have damaged many timbers but purpleheart is very stable. The accompanying graph was drawn to try to predict its final weight. The water in the glass represents the water lost over five months.*

chamber is nearly full. When more timber is present, less room is left for air. A small volume of air is limited in the speed with which it can draw water from a large volume of timber. For this reason, filling a kiln makes it more efficient and easier to control accurately.

In practice, timber at 20°C will stop a degree or two short of reaching equilibrium moisture content with respect to a certain R.H. value of air. This means that two samples of a timber, one dry the other moist, set in air of the same R.H. will finish up about 3% different in moisture content. This phenomenon is called 'hysteresis'.

If a timber is placed in a situation where the R.H. of the air does not match its moisture content to within 2%,it can lose or absorb moisture and change in dimensions. This shrinkage or swelling is referred to as 'movement', and can have a disastrous effect on fine cabinet work. Some timbers can be very problematic in this way, e.g. parana, while others give negligible problems, notably teak, afrormosia etc. In general, movement in use due to R.H. fluctuations corresponds to the radial and tangential shrinkage rates and the difference between them, but there are exceptions. Shrinkage is the dimension change going from green to 12% moisture. Movement is defined as the dimension change going from equilibrium with air at 90% R.H. to equilibrium with 60% R.H. air. Cherry has a high shrinkage rate but low movement, and among timbers generally the correlation between the two is not great. Methods can be applied during design and construction of a piece to minimise movement problems but this is beyond the scope of this book.

Overdrying of some timbers may, due to hysteresis, permanently reduce the equilibrium moisture content of a piece by 1–1.5% and render it less likely to movement due to normal R.H. fluctuations. This idea must be treated with caution as excess overdrying just gives a timber which will swell in use but, in general, cabinetwork timber is best dried slightly to the dry side of its theoretical requirements. Only kilning can do this.

British Standard 1186 (1971) states:

'The moisture content of the timber during manufacture and when handed over to the purchaser shall be within plus or minus 2 of the average equilibrium moisture content per cent that it is expected to attain in service . . .'

Fig. 92 *A PEG impregnated bowl turned in a manner impossible if the timber could shrink.*

An alternative to controlling moisture content is impregnation. Green or very moist timber is soaked in a solution of poly-ethylene glycol (called P.E.G.) in water. This treatment is also speeded up by raised temperatures which accelerate molecular movement. Once in place in the cell walls the P.E.G. holds the cellulose molecules apart even when the water is subsequently dried off. P.E.G. is not usually used on large boards or cabinetmaking timber because of the cost of the material and the need for large vats and long submersion periods. There is no reason why it should not be used for small-scale and model work by the woodworker with access to green timber. It is freely used by some for the preparation of green wood for turning. Its use allows wood to be turned in directions which would be impracticable with timber seasoned by drying methods.

CHAPTER 8

PESTS AND DECAY

In nature, all living things are subject to attack by parasites of various kinds and eventually to death. Both are natural processes, and through evolution, the individuals making up the natural community of a woodland have arrived at strategies for dealing with them. Living trees have defence mechanisms against parasitic invasion. Newly introduced parasites may kill a tree until a degree of immunity evolves on both sides to increase survival values. Thus Dutch

Fig. 93 *Decay fungi on dead wood.*

elm disease is lethal to our elms but not those in its country of origin. It is worth remembering that myxamatosis was nearly 100% lethal to rabbits but it is not nearly so high now.

Almost all life forms age and die and are then subject to decay. This decay is a vital part of the community and the saprovores which carry it out make the elements of the dead organism, notably its nitrogen, sulphur and phosphorus, available to the further growth of living things. The organisms which attack timber, and are seen as pests by users of wood, are essential to the woodland community which produces the timber. People acting as waste disposal or food distribution operatives in our society would not appreciate being regarded as pests.

The study of timber decomposers is simplified by the fact that only two types of organism are involved – insects and fungi. Both groups include parasites of the living tree as well as decomposers of dead ones. It is useful to understand something of their modes of operation.

Fungi reproduce by spores. These are microscopic, highly-resistant single cells which fungus fruit bodies, such as mushrooms and brackets, produce in billions. These spores are a ubiquitious feature of the air around us. When they settle onto a surface, they will take up moisture from it and start to grow a branched hair-like structure called the hypha. This exudes enzyme solutions onto the surface which will digest and dissolve specific food materials. These solutions will be absorbed as food for further hyphal growth until a branched network is formed – the mycelium. A patch of mould on bread is a mycelium. Fungi require oxygen to carry out this process.

The fungus spores will not produce a mycelium if any of the above stages are blocked. If wood does not contain at least 20% water, the spore cannot absorb enough. If its hyphae cannot find their required food materials, or if the enzymes are chemically blocked, no growth can take place. There may be toxic chemicals present or there may not be sufficient oxygen available. All of these suggest ways of discouraging fungi from attacking dead wood. It must be remembered that these fungi are already decomposing woody waste in soil and that, therefore, timber in contact with the soil is much more subject to vigorous attack. The standard test for a timber's durability is to bury an untreated 50×50mm heartwood section post to half its depth in soil and apply modest sidepressure periodically until it fails. Timbers are classified into durability classes of five year average life units.

Fig. 94 *Fungus spore germination.*

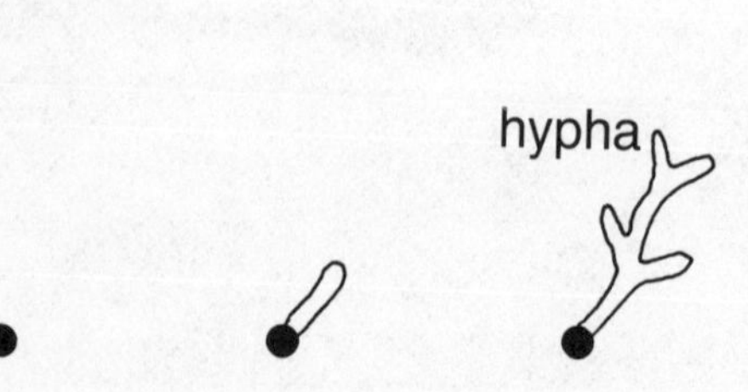

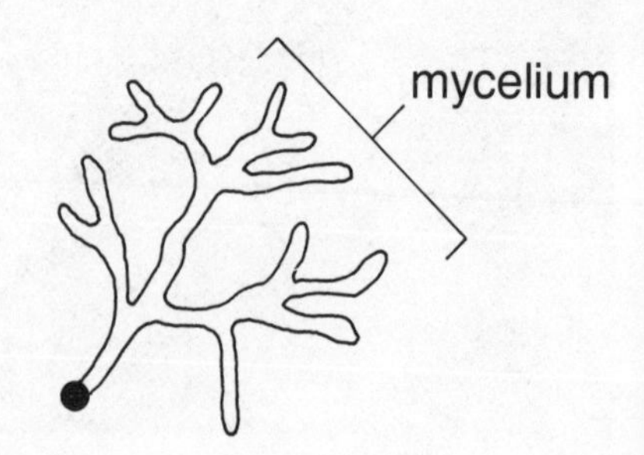

A few common timbers in their durability groupings:

under 5 yrs	5–10 years	10–15 years	15–25 yrs	25 yrs +
Ash	Elm	Keruing	Sweet chestnut	Afrormosia
Beech	Red Oak	Lauan	American mahogany	Afzelia
Birch	Obeche	African mahogany	White oak	Iroko
Sycamore	Poplar (most)	Meranti	Utile	Teak
Lime	Pines (most)	Walnut	W.R. Cedar	Greenheart
Plane	Spruce	Sapele	Pitch pine	Purpleheart
Willow		Cedar (most)	Yew	Padauk
				(no softwoods)

It may be noted that tropical timbers predominate towards the right. Even so, teak trunks do decay when they fall in the conditions found in teak forests.

Insects also have features in common in the way they affect timber. The overwhelming majority of temperate insects attack wood in their larval stages. The attack may be in the living tree as a parasite and is likely to render the trunk useless as timber, due to the network of holes the larvae bore. Goat moth larvae can do this to living oak, and woodwasp to various species of softwood. These do not attack dead timber although they are responsible for losses through write-offs of what the woodman may have believed to be good timber at the time of felling.

Fig. 95 *Goat moth damage in oak.*

Other insects, many of them also caterpillars, can damage the growth rate of a tree by seriously damaging its first flush of spring leaves. In this way oak may be largely defoliated in late April/May by the oak tortrix moth larvae. When populations are this large, a whole annual ring may be severely reduced in extent. The beneficiaries of this situation are the small birds of woodland which have spectacular breeding success in these years.

The beetle larvae that attack timber operate in much the same way but differ in the conditions needed and the timbers affected. They are distinguishable as adults but less so as larvae, although these are seldom seen. The damaged remains can be identified with guidance.

The commonest and most widespread is the furniture beetle or woodworm *Anobium punctatum*. It infests softwoods and temperate hardwood sapwood. Where fungi are also present, it may infect hardwood heartwood. It is less common in tropical hardwoods although it can attack mahogany occasionally. Its life cycle is usually three years, so exit holes appear when wood has been in use for some time. Cool

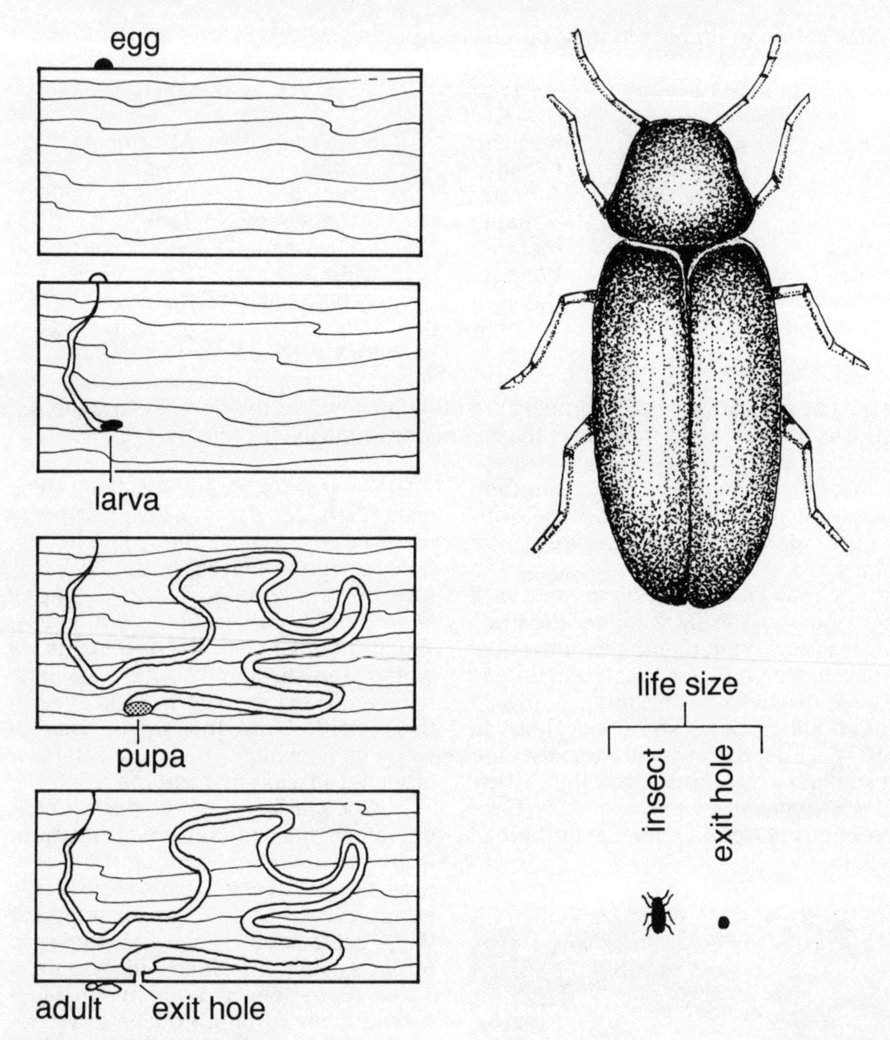

Fig. 96 *Life cycle of a furniture beetle.*
Fig. 97 *(right) Furniture beetle – woodworm* (Anobium punctatum).

conditions with some moisture favour its breeding, but its incidence has been decreased due to central heating and kilning of timber. Exit holes are 1–2mm diameter with crumbly-gritty yellowish frass (bore dust).

Related to *Anobium*, but less common, is the death watch beetle *(Xestobium rufovillosum)*. It is larger and confined to old and partially fungus-decayed hardwood, particularly oak. It is more a pest of stately homes than modern dwellings. Exit holes are about twice the size of woodworm holes and the frass is larger and contains visible spherical particles. But in some cases this creature may reproduce without emerging.

Lyctus brunneus and *L. linearis* are the powder post beetles which attack coarse textured hardwood sapwood, especially where these contain starch. Therefore the season of felling may affect the susceptibility to this pest. Its holes are the same size as those of *Anobium* and it is a similar, although slightly longer creature. Its frass is fine and talcy.

Fig. 98 *Common furniture beetle damage.* (photo courtesy Rentokil).

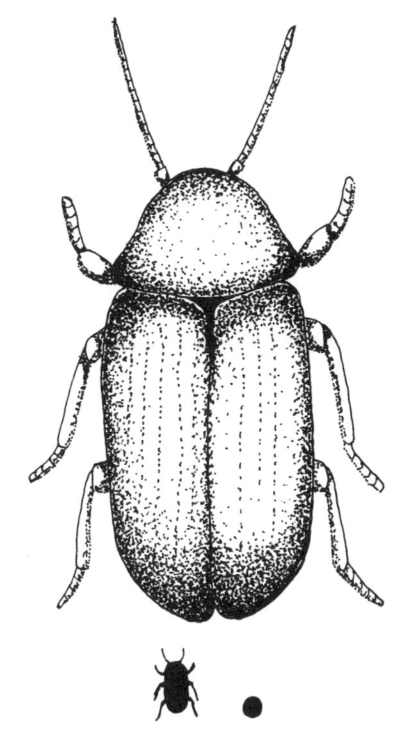

Fig. 99 *(left) Woodworm attack to underside of floorboard.*

Fig. 100 *(above) Death Watch beetle* (Xestobium rufovillosum).

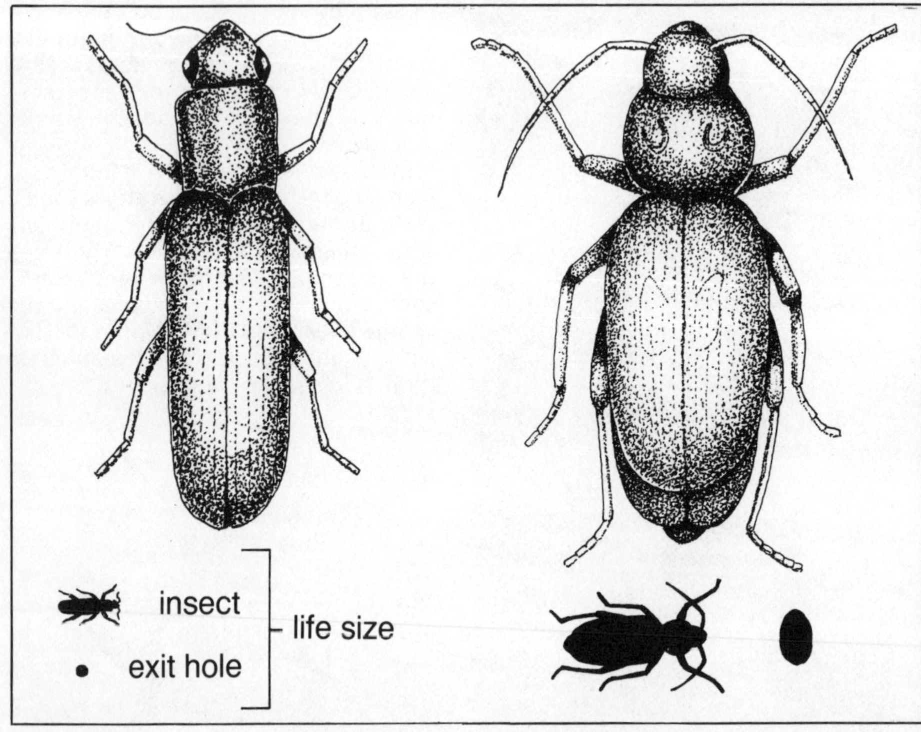

The house longhorn beetle is significantly larger than the above, at about 20mm long. It attacks softwood sapwood but requires very little moisture and so can attack properly dried woods in use and do extensive damage. it has an oval exit hole 6×9mm.

The ptilinus beetle may emerge from mid-European furniture timber, notably beech. Its feathery antennae distinguish it from *Anobium* and its holes are often rather tightly packed with frass.

There is a wide range of other creatures which may bore into wood or attempt to, but which are considered less significant. This is usually because they cause only secondary damage in fungus-decayed wood. The woodboring weevil is one of these and about the smallest which bores holes. When this creature is found, it is fungus infection which has to be treated rather than the weevil. Stagbeetle larvae can also be found under similar conditions although it is at the other end of the size range.

A range of other creatures may emerge from timbers imported from overseas. The jewel beetle may emerge from North American timber and the ambrosia beetle from various tropical parts, but neither is regarded as being a re-infection danger.

Another pest, not a beetle, is the sawfly. Its larvae normally feed on dock plants but will burrow into damp outdoor softwoods to pupate.

Two creatures commonly burrow into wood from seawater. These are the ter-

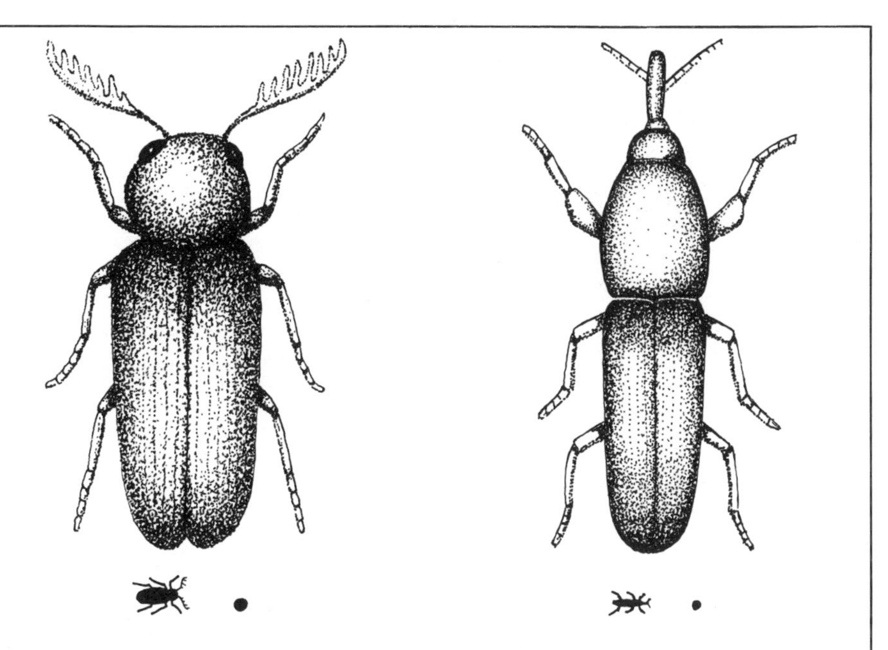

Fig. 101 *(opp left) Powderpost beetle* (Lyctus sp). **Fig. 102** *(opp right) House longhorn beetle.* **Fig. 103** *(above left) Ptilinus beetle* (Ptilinus sp). **Fig. 104** *(above right) Woodboring weevil* (Euophryum confine).

edo 'worm' (a mollusc) and the gribble (a crustacean). Some timbers are immune from their attacks, such as Australian turpentine and greenheart.

Fortunately Britain can forget the worst destroyer of timber worldwide which is the termite. We in Britain are known to complain about our climate but it has one redeeming feature – termites like it even less.

The major fungus in terms of damage potential is dry rot – *Serpula* (previously *Merulius*) *lachrymans*. Like any fungus, it requires at least 20% moisture to get established but its great damage potential is its ability to use the chemicals it extracts from damp wood to provide itself with surplus moisture to attack drier wood (hence 'dry' rot). Once star-

Fig. 105 *Teredo damage – Aberdovey harbour* (photo courtesy Rentokil)

Fig. 106 *Effect of dry rot.* (photo courtesy Rentokil)

ted, it is almost impossible to stop. It can produce highly resistant bootlace-like threads (*Rhizomorphs*) which can grow through intervening materials, like plaster and cracked brickwork, to seek and destroy new dry timbers. The mycelium is silky grey/white with suggestions of lemon or lilac shades. The fruit body resembles a firm pancake when young, but then becomes rust coloured as red/brown spores are produced in billions. It disintegrates wood into a crumbly mass split into cuboids and entirely devoid of strength. Removal of all contaminated wood and plaster and sterilisation of brickwork is carried out in its treatment.

More common, although less dreaded, are a number of fungi which cause what is called 'wet' rot. This signifies that they can only affect wood which has become sufficiently damp and do not extend into dry wood. They can be distinguished by their fruit bodies and by the texture of their mycelia and the damaged timber. Many have fruit bodies with pores from which the spores are released and thus 'poria' is often part of the latin name. There is *Poria placenta*

Fig. 107 *Dry rot fruiting bodies.* (photo courtesy Rentokil)

(the mine fungus) and *fibroporia vailantii, Donkioporia expansa* (white stringy rot). The identification of these is well documented but beyond the scope of this book.

Freshly-felled timber may be directly susceptible to a number of fungi and insects, which may damage it during the time it is awaiting conversion and drying. One method of protection is to submerge it in fresh water. This preserves it by depriving it of the free oxygen which both fungi and insects need. This is only intended as a short term measure but the existence of bog oak, and the preservation of the timbers of the *Mary Rose* ship, show its effectiveness. Most other preservation methods act by impregnating the timber with toxins.

One of the oldest preservation methods still in use is creosote – a mixture of coal tar derivatives obtained by distillation. As with any distillate, the temperature and conditions of the processing controls the nature of the end product. Creosote may be thin with low viscosity, or heavy in which case heat is necessary to provide the flow for its application. The chemistry of creosote is complex and so beyond this book.

Other preservatives are synthetic mixtures which may rely on fundamentally toxic elements for their effects, such as copper, chromium, mercury and arsenic. In some cases the preservatives are more complex organic compounds aimed at particular groups of organisms and specific aspects of their metabolism. In some cases insecticides may be very specific in their action on insects while leaving other types of organisms unharmed at the concentrations used. Unfortunately, not all have been so specific and benign.

Preservatives can be divided into two groups, with regard to solvent base. Some are dissolved in water. Water-soluble preservatives are usually the simpler inorganic compounds such as the popular copper chrome arsenic mixtures and the newer copper chrome boron formulations. The latter are said to be somewhat more heat stable, where heat is used to increase penetration, and slower to fix into cell walls. This slower fixation may also promote deeper penetration. In any case the Cu-Cr boron mixtures may be preferred to the more mammal-toxic arsenic in some applications. Borates have both insecticidal and fungicidal properties and so are sometimes used alone. These may be more complex chemicals such as disodium octaborate. Some organic compounds can be water-applied, e.g. sodium pentachlorophenoxide.

Other preservatives are applied dissolved in organic solvents. Pentachlorophenol is a typical fungicide which would be applied this way. Insecticides of organic solubility would include the chlorinated hydrocarbons such as lindane (gamma – chloro – cyclohexane) and dieldrin. The very water-insolubility of these chemicals, which caused the well publicised environmental disasters of their agricultural use, can be advantages in wood preservation. However lindane in particular is volatile and has received a very bad press for its effect on human operators and other susceptible animals, such as bats, which are under environmental pressure. Newer insecticides are organo-phosophorus and synthetic pyrethroids such as permethrin. These are regarded as more 'batsafe'.

Naphthenates are also used as preservatives. Copper naphthenate is used where colour does not matter (it is deep blue/green) and zinc napthenate; a little less effective but colourless. These work against insects and fungi. Organic tin compounds are also used, notably tributyl tin oxide (T.B.T.O.).

Fig. 108 *A Rentokil Property Care Technician, in full safety equipment, spraying the timbers in a roof void with woodworm fluid.* (photo courtesy Rentokil)

Each type has its own advantages and disadvantages. Creosote has volatile components which smell and may affect adjacent plant life; they leave a surface with some resistance to weathering but which cannot be painted; they may bleed into adjacent materials especially in hot climates;and they may increase inflammability.

Water-based preservatives may be transported dry and are easily made up. They are often odourless and can include fire retardents. Their main disadvantage is that they have to be used on well-dried timber for good penetration, but these timbers swell as they absorb water-based solutions and subsequently have to be redried. The preservatives may be water-soluble and leached out if in contact with rain.

Solvent-based formulations are more expensive and more flammable, at least during transport treatment and drying, but can carry water-insoluble compounds into the timber. They leave surfaces which can be treated in almost any way. There are also oil water emulsions of the consistency of mayonnaise which can be used to give very high surface loadings of preservatives, and are often the best form to pressure load into insect-bored wood.

The problem with all of these is that the wood itself is not blotting paper. It can be very resistant to the flow of liquids. Some timbers are much more resistant than others. Green timber may be extremely impermeable due to its water content. When dried, heartwoods are more resistant than sapwoods due to the chemicals dumped into them and the fact that most of the pits between adjacent tracheids are closed off (aspirated) (see page 11). The size and distribution of vessels affects the flow of liquid along the timber. In some cases quite large vessels are blocked off by tyloses (see p. 63). For this reason, red oaks are permeable to preservatives while white oaks are highly resistant. English oak heartwood is so resistant that old timbers which have been treated can be found with the sapwood still intact but the heartwood, despite its natural durability, rotted away.

To try to overcome such problems, various methods are used to increase preservative penetration. Soaking for long periods and squirting it on (flooding) at high velocity do little to really impermeable timbers. Pressure variation methods are more effective. These involve placing timber in metal pressure tanks, filling them with the preservative and then raising the pressure to force the liquid along the wood fibres. Two of the standard methods here are the TANALITH and CELLCURE treatments, widely used in the preservation of timber for fencing, building and agricultural applications. TANALITH C and CELLCURE A are copper-chrome-arsenic formulations dissolved in water which achieve a very high level of insoluble fixation in timber. They are not washed out and, in testing for agricultural suitability, have been fed as sawdust to livestock. They remain unaffected by the toxic elements so complete is its fixation into the molecular structure of the wood.

This kind of treatment is also used with organic solvent formulae which are more suitable for indoor timbers and those intended for furniture use and/or painting, for reasons given above. Greater sophistication is used in the pressure treatment with this method. The chamber, once loaded and sealed, is subjected to reduced pressure to suck some of the air out of the timber. The preservative is then added to the chamber and positive pressure applied to force it into the fibres of the wood. There is little air left in the timber to become pressurised and prevent liquid penetration to the centre. Once penetration is achieved, there is no need for expensive preservative to be left in the xylem elements so reduced pressure is applied once again to suck excess liquid back out of the timber. This double vacuum concept is given the name VAC-VAC for Hickson's version of this pressure treatment. CELPAK is the name for Rentokil's system, the end product of which is marketed under the name of SUPATIMBA.

TANALITH, TANALITH C and VAC-VAC are trademarks of Hickson Timber Products Ltd. CELLCURE, CELLCURE A, CELPAK and SUPATIMBA are trademarks of Rentokil Ltd.

CHAPTER 9

THE CONSERVATION PROBLEM

Within the UK, timber harvesting is difficult to sustain. It has been confused by the ravages of Dutch elm disease and will probably be affected for some time by the southern counties' gales of Oct '87. It is further confused if one tries to analyse the statistics on the subject by the quotation of woodland areas and replanting in hectares while yields are in metres^3.

Forestry Commission figures do suggest a sustainability of sorts in softwoods fuelling a burgeoning processing industry in some areas. But this must be weighed against the fact that 88% approximately of the softwood used in Britain is imported. Felling and use of British hardwoods follows various rather localised patterns and, as mentioned, is difficult to quantify. It is heartening to see the Forestry Commission increasingly using hardwood planting to break up their ecologically blanketing stands of conifer, but perhaps too early to see what effect this will have on supply and demand in the next century. It is heartening too to see moves toward encouraging the greater use of land for timber rather than fuelling food mountains. The farm woodland scheme does not necessarily appeal to all. It may change the emphasis in estate management but it will not touch the arable farm scene in its present form. Care is also needed that well-meaning legislation is not misused, as it was until recently in parts of the north of Scotland. Where financial incentives are used, it is important that they are geared to the real management needs of woodland, otherwise trees may be planted but not given the maintenance they need to mature usefully. It is vital that schemes, once introduced, are kept up. Governments and ideologies change on a shorter rotation than timber crops.

In some cases, conservation measures tend to work to the detriment of the trees themselves. In some localities, trees have been preserved as amenities too far into old age. Mature trees should be harvestable to become other things of use and beauty. Specimens like the 'Major' oak, propped and crutched into geriatric decrepitude, must be of questionable aesthetic appeal and are distinctly unsafe. It is thought by some that a proportion of overmature trees exacerbated the October '87 gale damage in parts of the south of England, large trees bringing others down with them.

While sustainability is desirable in forestry as in other areas, bearing in

Fig. 109 *Forest clearing for farms – buffer zone Mundemba Cameroon.* (photo courtesy M. Rautkari/WWF).

mind the vast volumes of timber which change country between tree and product, and the tiny proportion of our woodland left to us, it is parochial to become overly concerned with British timber sustainability. The real area of concern is global.

There is considerable concern for the amount of forest on our planet as a whole. Trees serve two main functions outside of timber production – they reverse the changes which animals and fuel burning have on the atmosphere and they absorb carbon dioxide extremely effectively, even when it is present in concentrations as low as 1 part in 5000 or less. They pass out oxygen in return. In this way the whole carbon cycle is powered. As forests decline worldwide, there is concern that a carbon dioxide build-up may cause the 'greenhouse effect'. This is an increased trapping of the sun's energy by slowing its release into space, thus possibly raising the overall atmospheric temperature. Quite small temperature changes could change weather patterns and may be partly responsible for changes in rainfall patterns which have had such catastrophic human effects in parts of Africa.

As I mentioned in Chapter One, trees maintain a large upward flow of soil water and push it into the atmosphere in transpiration. Trees are much the most effective plant forms in this respect and in this way keep the water cycle going. Their deep roots put in a demand for soil water which raises the water table to the point where lesser-rooted plants can obtain it. Without trees our planet could become as desert as Frank Herbert's science-fiction novel *Dune* – a planet with water, but none of it being recycled. It was portrayed as similar to Sahara dunesand, but planetwide.

This is more than just a fanciful possibility. In certain rainforest areas – sources of our most prized timbers – forest clearance has been as catastrophic as this. Rainforest has some features rather different from our woodlands. Typically, rainforest may receive 500 inches of rain a year, an amount beyond the average Westerner's comprehension. Plant growth is so lush in these temperatures and humidities that soil nutrients are absorbed by plants as they are formed from rapid humus breakdown. Very little is left in the soil. Rainfall beats upon the foliage but never reaches the soil direct. If all the trees are removed from an area, a thin, poorly fertile soil is left which could be easily washed away by direct torrential rain. This rapid soil removal can silt up lower areas of the watershed causing subsequent flooding elsewhere. Where this clearance is done for agricultural 'development', woodwaste is generally burned to release some soil minerals. Too often, the agriculture practised will not protect the soil or maintain normal recycling of nutrients and fails after a season or two, leaving an area which has no chance of regenerating forest and very little of returning to agricultural usefulness. The farmer may have had to move on to repeat the process in order to grow any crops. This is known as 'slash and burn' agriculture. If it spreads over a large enough area, even the rainfall may fail.

Primitive societies can maintain themselves in rainforests in total harmony with their environment but, when 'development' and population overspills occur, events seldom allow this harmony to continue. This is why there is such widespread concern about the Indonesian transmigration plan. The Indonesian government raised plans to alleviate overcrowding in Java and Bali by spreading 65,000,000 people across the forested islands of Sumatra, Kalimantan Sulowesi and Irian Jaya. Despite an official grand plan of words, this seemed almost certain to defoliate these islands with a desperate slash and burn attempt to feed a growing expatriate population, while displacing the people who can live in the environment without damaging it, the indigenous population. Fortunately, this plan has been cut back drastically but, despite lobbying, the World Bank has not cut the aid input to this scheme and it is still in progress, albeit more slowly than originally planned.

In parts of Central and South America, much of the clearance has been an attempt to develop cattle ranching due to an apparently lucrative US demand for beef. On the kinds of soils left by forest clearance, it is doubtful if beef production could compare with well-managed forestry.

Where does the timber trade and user stand in responsibility for this shortsightedness? Clearly, when timber is

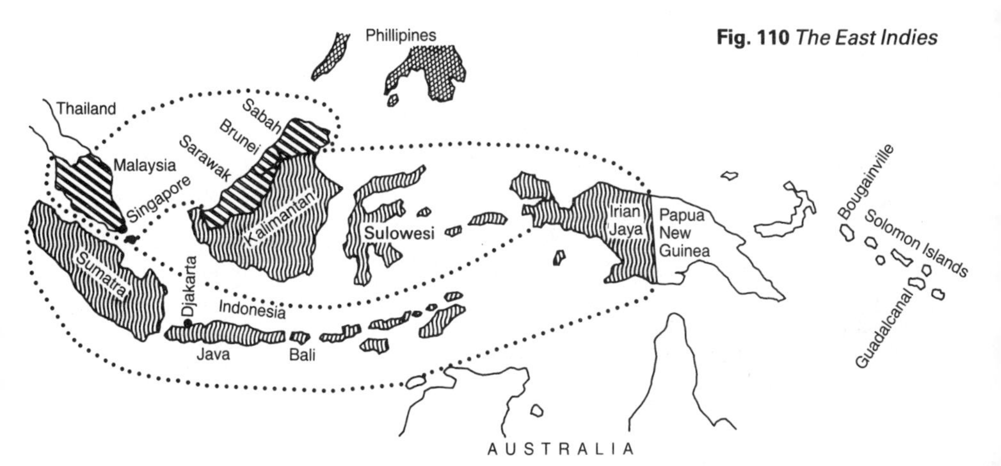

Fig. 110 *The East Indies*

felled for whatever reason, there will not be a shortage of people willing to deal in it for profit, and there will always be a proportion for whom profit considerations will overide all else. Timber stands are the property and responsibility of the government of the land but the nature of, and the pressures on, Third World governments often dictate short term measures and profits. Some of the pressures on Third World governments have their origins in the developed world.

Another characteristic of tropical forest affects the situation here. Temperate woodland may be a stand of 20 species of woody plants, with two or three predominating. In equatorial rainforest, there are no dominant species and species numbers can be astronomical. There may be more species of trees within a few hectares than there are total plant species in the British Isles. This means that a given species is widely dispersed and a majority of those in between are not desirable and may be of little use other than firewood.

Some may be good timber but may be overlooked due to ignorance of their possibilities. This means that logging roads have to be cut through the forest to extract a few trees here and there. This should leave a forest with a few linear, cleared areas capable of full regeneration by natural means. In many areas, however, withdrawal of what may have been a perfectly responsible logging operation may be followed by an influx down its logging roads of local populations who continue cutting for fuelwood or slash and burn agriculture. This effectively destroys a forest which the logging concern left capable of further production. This kind of destruction is usually a failure of government regulations or their policing, but the developed world's desire for these few trees above all others may be held to be the spark.

The timber trading organisations feel that logging is not the prime cause of deforestation, pointing to the facts that in most tropical countries less than 10% of timber felled is exported and 90% is burned as fuelwood. But in some cases the 10% may represent the good timber, the remaining 90% being fuelwood, resulting in 100% deforestation. The

Fig. 111 *Logging road – Kwam-koro, Tanzania* (photo courtesy WWF/Jill Lovett)

problems will differ depending on the part of the world as will the efforts made to remedy the situation.

The government of Malaysia have taken the lead in improving the situation. They have carried out full investigations into all the possible uses of the trees in their forests. A leaflet has been produced showing the colour and figure, and giving the basic properties and uses of over fifty timbers. The ability to utilise this many timbers (although only a small proportion of the species present) reduces the area disturbed for a given timber yield and thus allows longer regeneration cycles. It also increases the possibilities of creating plantations which work and would show some degree of wildlife diversity. Normally, rainforest trees cannot be plantationed in monocultures without falling prey to parasite epidemics.

Malaysia has also replaced some of its felled forest with rubber plantation, which has certain advantages over some kinds of agriculture. It is forest-like cover and hence protects and utilises the soil well. This is no real replacement for virgin forest, with its beautiful diversity, but it is an improvement on exposed soil. It is also the basis of a healthy and sustainable industry which creates employment. Finally, at the end of the life of the plantation, it yields a timber which Malaysia is thoroughly researching and promoting and which looks highly useful. Malaysia has the advantage of a basic industrial development based on Japanese technology, which both helps to keep the pressure off landspace and produces a financial situation conducive to funding forestry research.

Unfortunately in Sarawak, under the auspices of the same government, things appear to be going less well. Some logging concessions are vigorously opposed by indigenous populations with nothing more than squatters rights to their native lands. This is the home of the world's ramin, a swamp forest timber which now seems to be approaching commercial extinction because of lack of management.

Sustainability is held to be possible in virtually all rainforest sites but in most parts of the world it is still only a hope for the future. It must be almost a reality in peninsular Malaysia, parts of India and Burma and possibly Java, most of them in terms of teak. For most of the desirable tropical hardwoods it is not the case and should we perhaps be using these particular timbers or attempting some form of boycott of Brazilian, African and Phillipine mahogany?

'Yes' say Friends of the Earth; 'No' says the Timber Trades Federation. Despite the financial interest of the latter, their approach may be the more positive. Awareness of the problem is increasing worldwide, not least due to the work of the International Timber Trade Organsiation I.T.T.O. This organisation may have made a somewhat faltering start and is, by its constitution, dominated by the Japanese who are seen as tropical timber greedy, being importers of about half the total internationally-traded tropical timber. However, its motivation toward sustainability is no less for this. Its approach is that, if we withdraw from markets, we also withdraw from effective conversation about supplies with the countries concerned. Britain is a small importer of these timbers on the world scale and its withdrawal would be meaningless. If the hardwood importing nations as a whole boycotted suppliers, this would render the stands of fine tropical timber valueless to their owners and this could only increase the chances that they would fall to other uses both sustainably and ecologically less desirable. If we continue to trade, it will be worthwhile for producer countries to nurture their stocks. We must be willing to pay realistic prices but there is some evidence to this fact. One of the most expensive timbers, but one in which there is considerable international trade, is teak: one of the few tropical timbers which, in parts at least, is being sustainably produced. If, by good communication, we can bring together a willingness to buy at realistic prices with a producer country's willingness to supply intelligently, we can create a basis in some Third World countries of an industry which will support their populations far better than slash and burn agriculture. One of the first aims here must be internationally-recognised labelling of supply sources so that we know where a timber comes from. If we are to boycott anything, perhaps it should be the beefburger, but that would only benefit rainforests if we were sure it was Central American beef.

Sustainable sources must be seen internationally to be encouraged and, in this context, the timbers of the United States, both hardwood and softwood, are being promoted. They come from a source which is capable of much higher yields than are currently being cut. They cannot be looked upon as direct substitute for tropical timbers as most are clearly temperate in nature and figure but they are highly varied and there is no shortage of property information about them.

The wood user concerned about these problems should seek constructive conversation with his or her supplier as a first stage to being aware of sources of supply and making them aware of user feelings. Unless specifically traditional methods are felt essential, the wood user should ensure that they are operating in the twentieth century and making sensible use of modern laminates and veneers.

APPENDIX 1
NOTES ON SOME COMMONLY USED TIMBERS

Ash (*Fraxinus excelsior* – European ash) There are several American species.

Ash is the most elastic and tough W. European timber. It is markedly ring porous with no visible heartwood boundary. It is not durable for outdoor use. Its density is about 0.6 at 12% moisture although this varies markedly with speed of growth (see page 44). It needs some care in seasoning as it shrinks appreciably.

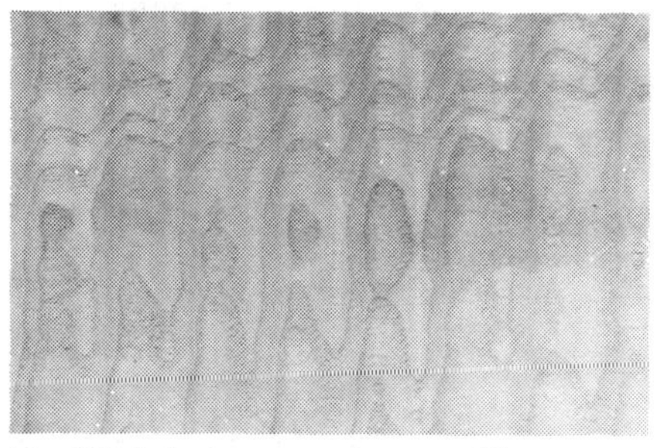

Fig. 112 *Ash veneer – an unusual figure known as 'ribbled ash' (Japanese origin).*

It turns very well, works easily and is widely used for furniture where its attractive but delicate growth ring markings are best seen on almost tangential faces. For this reason, it is often used as veneer on furniture. It has an attractive clean straw colour with occasional suggestions of grey-brown or pink. It is sometimes ebonised for furniture use. It steam bends excellently. It has appreciable ray tissue although this is almost invisible.

It presents no problem with finishing, although the coarse uneven texture leaves pores which can become ingrained with dirt in some cases if not grain filled or finished to a smooth surface. Drying oil type finishes are not recommended for this reason.

Beech (*Fagus sylvatica*)
Beech is a very smooth-textured, diffuse, porous timber of considerable strength and rigidity. It is very rapidly weathered and deteriorated by exterior conditions unless very thoroughly preserved and its best use is therefore indoors. Its density is about 0.65 at 12%.

It turns quite well – some feel better when green than seasoned. It may be evenly neutral to straw colour, or with uneven grey-brown or pinkish streaks. Steaming accentuates an even pink colouration. It steam-bends well and works very smoothly with ease.

It is mostly used for commercial furniture production where it often gains coloured finishes of dubious depth and aesthetic value. It is worthy of showing

Fig. 113 *Beech after five days outdoors in showery weather.*

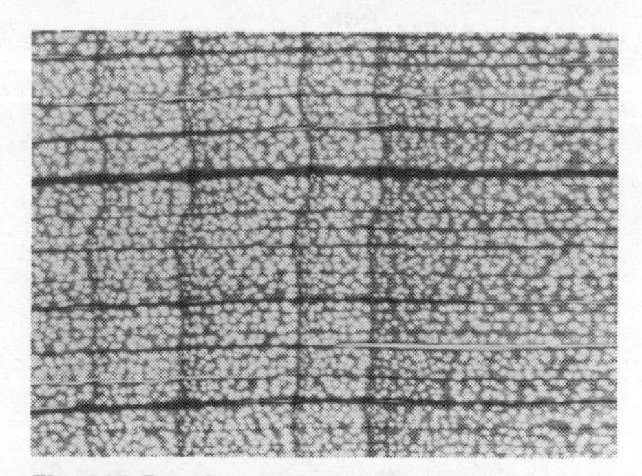

Fig. 114 *Beech cross section.*

its own grain since, like oak but on a smaller scale, it has an attractive ray figure. It is an excellent choice for indoor cabinetwork and finishes in any style with no problems. It was the material of the traditional English plane.

Birch (*Betula* – several species)
Birch is a diffuse porous timber of S.G. about 0.5. It is not durable outdoors. It is not widely available in large sizes and a majority of the commercial timber goes for the best grade of interior ply construction.

It is a pale straw colour with little figure. Its bark is a source of tannin in places.

Cherry (*Prunus spp* – notably *avium*) – many American *spp*.

Cherry is a strong, moderately hard, diffuse to slightly ring porous timber. The sapwood is straw-coloured with an attractive pink, through to occasionally almost mahogany-coloured heartwood.

Its density is about 0.55. It is not durable outdoors.

It turns and works very well but may be a little problematic for very fine surface finishing. It is a very fine cabinetwork timber but one requiring care in seasoning.

It is closely related to apple (*Malus spp*), pear (*Pyrus* spp) and plum (also *Prunus* sp) which vary from the above description mainly in shades of colour.

Chestnut
There are two chestnuts – sweet and horse. They bear little similarity to each other.

Sweet chestnut (*Castanea sativa*) is a markedly ring porous timber often described as oak without the silver grain. Like oak, it contains tannins and is moderately durable for outdoor use, although generally slightly lower in density at about 0.6. It is easier to season. It is widely used for chestnut fencing (see Chapter Three)

Horse chestnut (*Aesculus hippocastanum*). Apart from a pale straw colour sometimes made use of in veneer, this timber seems to have little to commend it. It is rather like a light porous birch.

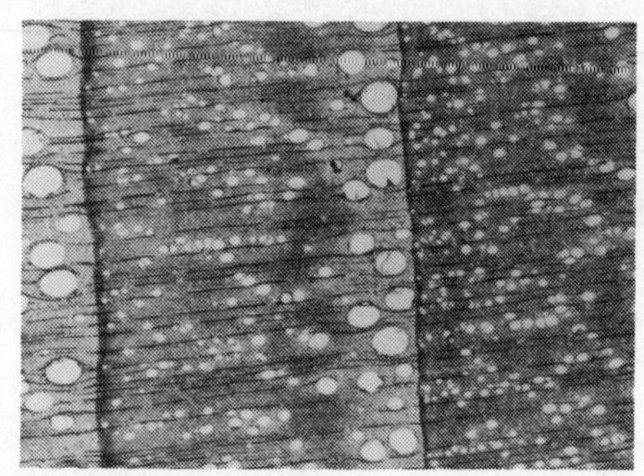

Fig. 115 *Sweet chestnut.*

Elm (*Ulmus spp* – notably *procera*)
Elm is an elastic and tough timber, moderately hard and resistant to splitting due to crossed grain (Chapter Five). It is moderately durable outdoors, if not wetted and dried in ground contact. Thoroughly wet, it is durable and early water pipes were made from it. Its S.G. is about 0.6. It can have a blunting effect on tools although it is otherwise fairly

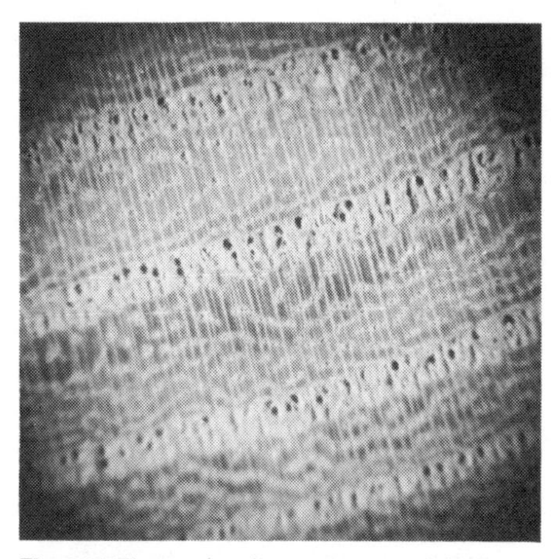

Fig. 116 *Elm endgrain – compare with* **Fig 19** *(bottom right) on page 20.*

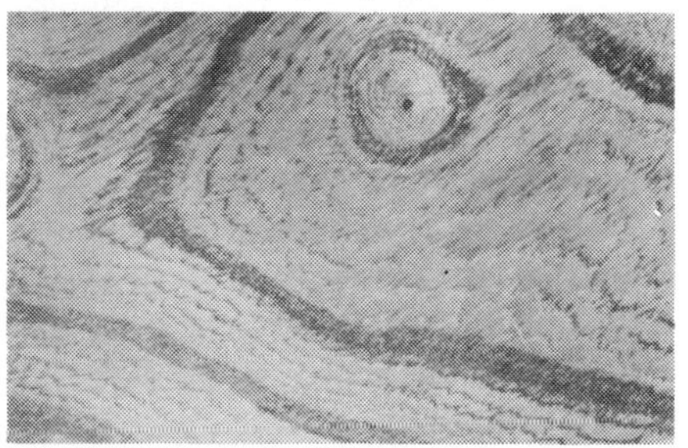

Fig. 117 *Elm – partridge breast figure.*

easily workable. It is a mid to red-brown with an attractive 'partridge breast' figure due to its pattern of vessel and parenchyma production.

It turns excellently. Due to massive losses of trees due to Dutch elm disease there has been a glut, which is now largely over, leaving it in short supply in places.

Hornbeam (*Carpinus betulus*)
Hornbeam is a fine, even-textured and very hard wood with no visible heartwood. It is dense at about 0.75.

It turns quite well and can be used for cabinetwork if its relatively small sizes are acceptable. It has been compared in working properties to densest beech although it has less figure, since the ray structure is not picked out by colour or light reflection.

Its split resistant cross-graining and smooth texture have made it ideal for small wooden mechanical parts. Wooden screws, cogs and bobbin parts are its particular application, and many piano black keys are hornbeam in disguise. It needs a hard finish. Drying oil finishes tend to leave it looking grubby.

Lime (*Tilia vulgaris, cordata* and *platyphylla*)
Lime is fine and even-textured but soft and rather light with an S.G. of 0.4 or below. It is a little too soft to turn well but its particular application is for carving. It

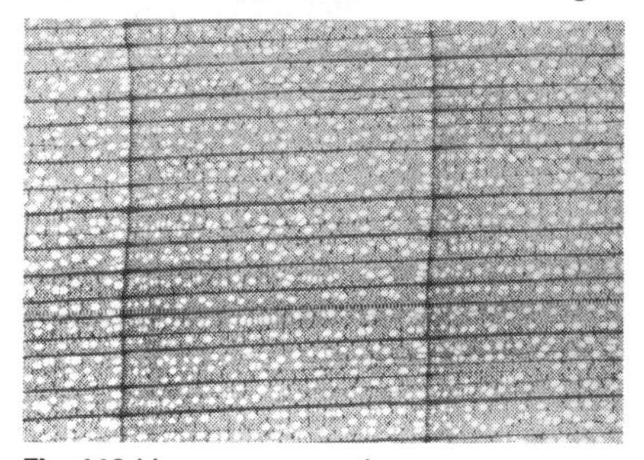

Fig. 118 *Lime – cross section.*

is a fairly even fawn colour with a small slightly darker ray system. It seems to have been Grinling Gibbons' favourite material.

Mahogany
The question is – what is mahogany? A wide variety of timbers from all over the world have had the name mahogany applied to them. The original mahogany was *Swietenia mahogani* – Cuban mahogany – now commercially extinct. The proliferation of the name mahogany

was consequent upon attempts to replace it. Its most legitimate relative is *Swietenia macrophylla* from Central America and North Amazonia. This is softer and lighter than the original. S.G. around 0.55 but variable.

Two African genera may be included as mahoganies. Khaya (*Khaya* spp) but also some species of *Entandrophragma* are marketed as African mahogany, which can therefore be a rather variable product. Some types are of quite low density.

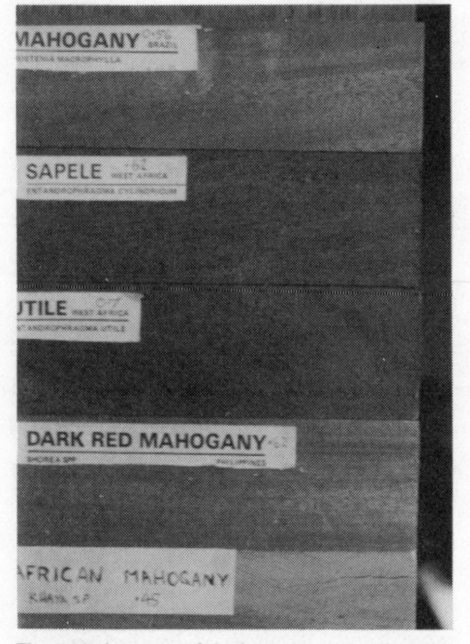

Fig. 119 *A range of timbers sometimes called mahogany.*

Two *Entandrophragma* species tend now to be marketed under their own names – *E. utile* (pronounced You-tilly) and *E. cylindricum* – sapele (pronounced Sap-eelee). Utile is denser and easier to season but less decoratively figured (see p. 48).

These three genera are generally accepted as mahogany. They are all red-brown, not very hard and with interlocked grain making them difficult to plane well. They are closely related in the botanical family of *Meliaceae*. Also in this family is the Australian rose mahogany (*Dysoxylum* sp) but this is not generally available in this country.

Also sometimes called mahogany are some of the Indonesian and Phillipine timbers of the *Dipterocarp* group. This is biologically less legitimate although some do seem to have the same general colour and characteristics. Keruing (*Dipterocarpus* spp) is a particularly dense and dark member of this group. Meranti (*Shorea* spp – mostly) often called Phillipine mahogany or dark red mahogany is superficially very like the legitimate mahoganies although the lighter merantis, lauan and seraya (all *Shorea* or *Parashorea* spp) are lighter, softer and hardly compare with real mahoganies.

All work and turn well and finish nicely with almost any material.

Oak (*Quercus* – many spp)
Widespread across the northern hemisphere.

Oaks are all ring porous with two sizes of rays. All are hard and dense and have been widely used as structural materials. They are also used decoratively due to their 'silver grain' on quarter cut surfaces. Red oaks (*Q rubra*) are porous with no tyloses in their vessels.

White oaks (e.g. *Q. robur* and *Q. petraea*) have these tyloses and are thus very impenetrable to preservatives. They are equally impenetrable to water and so find one of their main applications in cooperage (barrels).

All contain tannin and its interaction with some chemicals causing staining are dealt with in Chapter Six.

Oak may also be coloured by a fungus infection –*Fistulina hepatica*. This gives

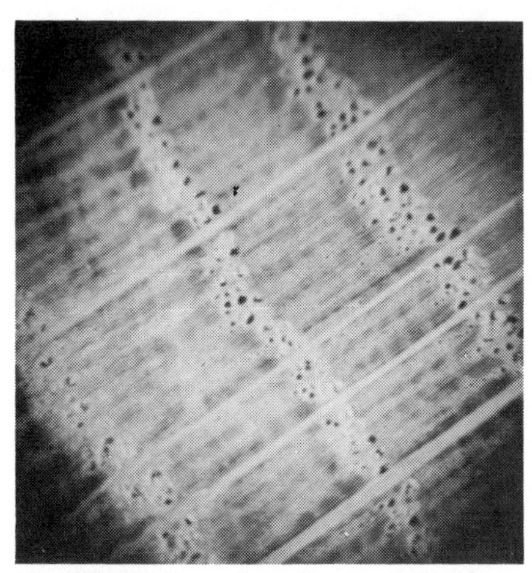

Fig. 120 *Handlens view of endgrain in oak (see also* **Figs. 20(a)** *and* **(b)** *and* **Fig. 83***).*

brown oak – a much prized colour variation with only a little reduction in strength.

English oak can be a little difficult to work. It is very hard and the large rays can be very different in working texture from the axial system. It turns quite well in large sizes although small turnings can be difficult to finish due to the rays and coarse texture.

Japanese oak (*Q. mongolica*) is slightly easier to work due to its finer, more even texture. It is a particularly even straw colour with rays smaller than English oak.

Pine (*Pinus sylvestris*)
Widespread across N. Eurasia. Pine is our most used timber in terms of amount. The building and D.I.Y. trade use it almost exclusively for most work. S.G. is between 0.4 – 0.5. It is not very durable outdoors untreated but is very amenable to preservative treatment, and can make successful garden furniture. It is used for indoor furniture and cabinetwork. It works easily if not too knotty and finishes well, although it is really rather too soft for furniture in daily use and does tend to surface mark too easily. It can be turned with care.

It can have a wide range of attractive colours from straw, through yellow to pink-red and dark browns with occasional blue-grey stains in sapwood.

It has a nicely accentuated figure of growth rings but can be very knotty – attractive decoratively perhaps, according to taste but weaker structurally. It can be excessively resinous causing finishing problems, particularly with paint.

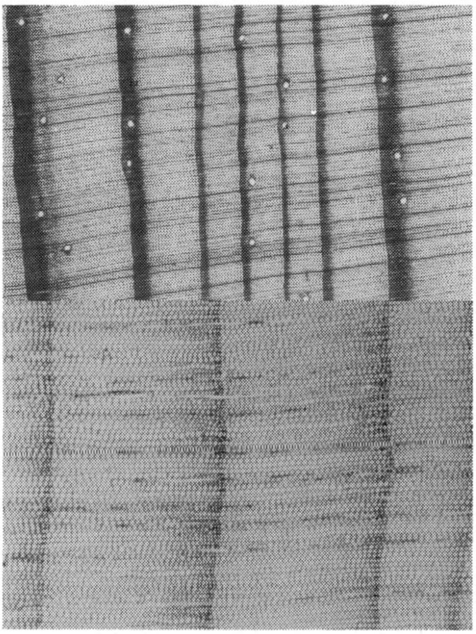

Fig. 121 *(above) Scots pine (European redwood,* Pinus sylvestris*) – note resin canals (Scandinavia/USSR). (below) Parana (Parana pine,* Araucaria spp) – Amazonia (see **Fig 14***)*

Occasionally joinery softwood may not be pine. Hemlock (*Tsuga spp*) is sometimes found. It is less resinous and knotty but does not work and finish as well.

Parana (*Aruacaria brasiliana*) may also be found. It can be quite similar to knotless pine with only very faint growth rings. It works and finishes excellently but it can move alarmingly in use.

Sycamore (*Acer pseudoplatanus*)
Sycamore is a pale lustrous timber with little growth ring figure and a small although distinctly decorative ray figure. It is not durable outdoors. Its density is usually between 0.6 – 0.7. It is diffuse porous and fine and even of texture.

It needs much care in seasoning and handling to prevent staining ruining its beautifully pale colour.

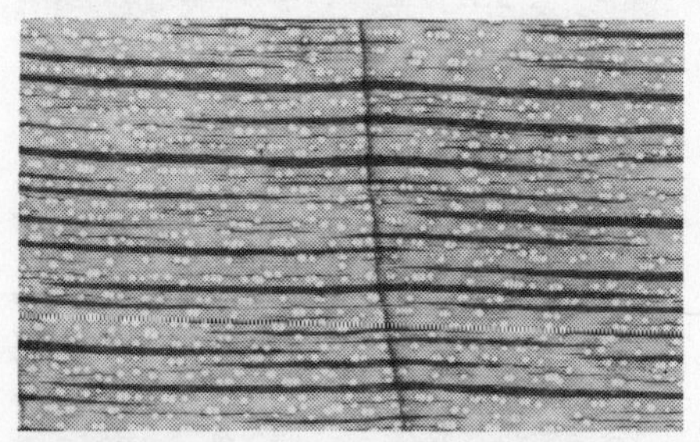

Fig. 122 *Sycamore – cross section. Note – the rays do not begin and end but wander up and down out of the plane of the section.*

It turns very well, works well in cabinetwork and finishes easily. It was used in times gone by for domestic woodware, as it scrubs clean easily and with minimum detriment to its structure and surface. It may exhibit fiddleback grain in radial section.

Teak
This is almost the same situation as in mahogany. A variety of timbers belong to what can be thought of as the teak group, although they are more likely to go under their own names rather than masquerading as teak.

All have features clearly in common. They shrink very little on seasoning and move very little in use. They tend to have mineral inclusives and thus blunt tools to some extent. They all seem to be within a recognisable colour range between a coffee and honey colour. All belong to the highest durability class. Having so much in common it is surprising that they are not at all closely related.

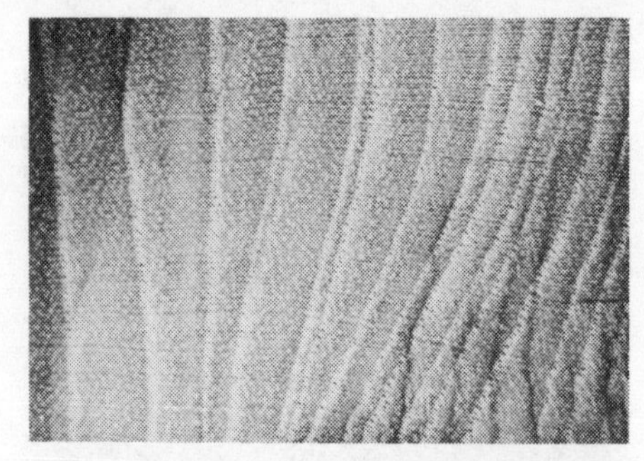

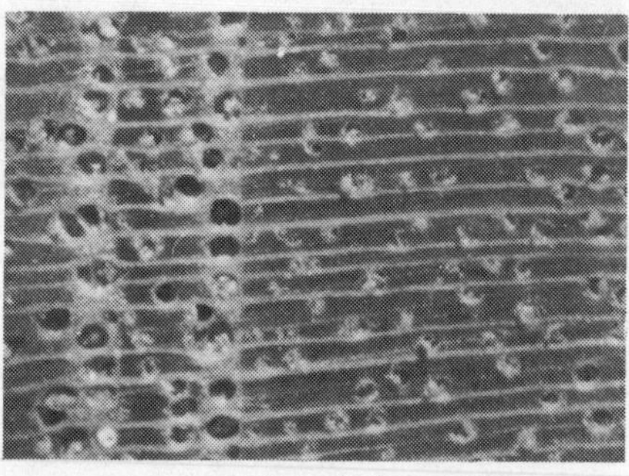

Fig. 123 *(above) Teak endgrain. (below) Teak endgrain – note one mineral filled vessel.*

Teak (*Tectona grandis*) *Verbenaceae* – originally S.E. Asia but now plantationed in many parts of the world. Ring porous with growth rings, Oily – some glue-finishing problems possible (see Chapter Six). Very decorative and ideal for furniture inside and out.

Iroko (*Chlorophora excelsa*) *Moraceae* (closely related to elm) E. and W. Africa. Coarse diffuse porous. Easily distin-

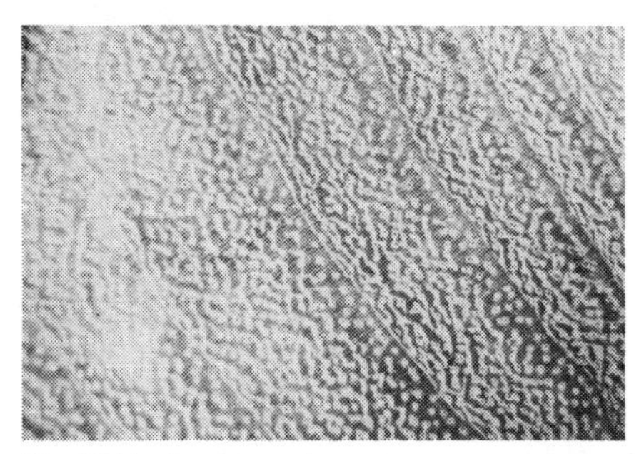

Fig. 124 *Iroko endgrain.*

guished by pale parenchyma lines. Less decorative for indoor furniture.

Afrormosia (*Pericopsis elate*) W. Africa. Fine diffuse porous. Less blunting effect than teak. Used indoors and out. Less marked than teak.

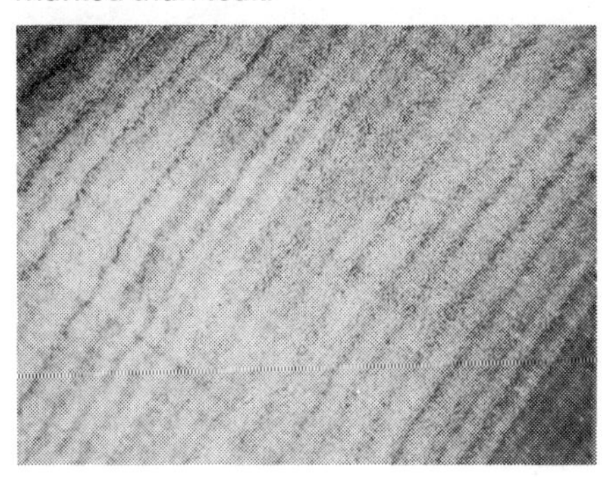

Fig. 125 *Afrormosia endgrain.*

Afzelia (*Afzelia spp*) C. and W. Africa. Fine diffuse porous. Redder than the above.

The latter two are closely related to each other, although not the first two. Both are members of the very large group the *Leguminosae.*

Walnut (*Juglans regia*)
Europe to W. Asia. Also American species.

Walnut is a rather coarse-textured

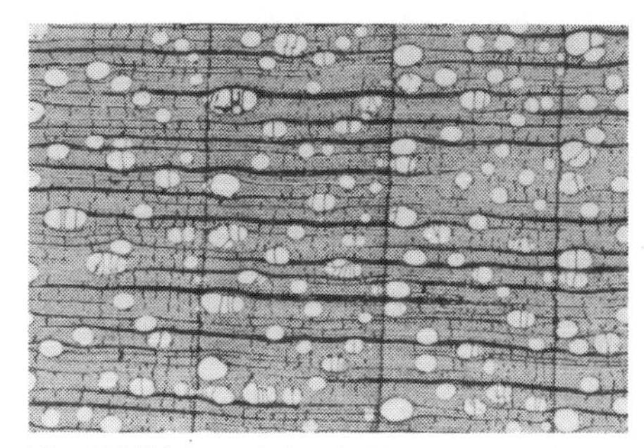

Fig. 126 *Walnut endgrain.*

timber, somewhere between ring and diffuse porous. It has a grey-to-straw coloured sapwood with a darker warm toned heartwood, sometimes attractively streaked with darker brown. S.G. is about 0.65.

It is easy to work for turning and cabinetwork and is highly prized for both. It finishes well with no problems. Its resilience and shock resistance make it a special timber for gunstocks.

African walnut (*Lovoa trichilioides*). Closely related to the mahoganies with interlocked stripe figure well developed. Apart from a generally warm brown tone, it seems to have little to do with walnut.

Willow (*Salix spp*)
Europe and Asia. A soft and light timber – S.G. only about 0.35. Pale in colour with very little figure. Apart from cricket bats, it has no specific application.

Yew (*Taxus bacata*)
Britain and Europe. Yew is one of the most elegant timbers. It is a close, fine textured softwood. It is quite dense at about 0.7 and fairly hard. It is reasonably durable outdoors. It is very straightforward to work with, turns beautifully and it steam bends very well.

There is a narrow pale sapwood. The

heartwood carries a marvellous range of colours from pink through orange to teak and mahogany shades.

Other timbers mentioned in the text:
Alder (*Alnus glutinosa*)
British and European riverside tree. Has been used for clog soles.

Hazel (*Corylus avellana*)
Britain. Various rural uses in the past for coppiced hazel sticks.

Hawthorn (*Crataegus spp*)
Britain. Fine yellow-white wood but limited application due to small sizes.

Maple (*Acer spp*)
Europe and America. Relatives of sycamore. Very many species, each with its own properties.

Plane (*Platanus acerifolia*)
Britain. Some American species. Also called lacewood. Extremely even dark rays give a fine figure on radial surfaces. Turns very decoratively and, like sycamore, is resistant to being scrubbed.

Poplar (*Populus* – many species)
Related to willow. Not very fine or of particular application.

Douglas fir (*Pseudotsuga menziesii*)
USA. A strong softwood, much veneered for construction ply. Can be a highly growth ring figured timber.

Larch (*Larix decidua*)
Unusual conifer in that it is deciduous. Strong and resilient. Highly growth ring figured.

Pitch Pine (*Pinus spp*)
USA. The hardest and most resinous pine.

Spruce (*Picea spp* – notably *sitchensis*).
Lighter, less-figured softwood much used for paper and as industrial roundwood.

Yellow Pine (*Pinus spp* e.g. *strobus*).
Lighter, less-figured pine of very even texture. Carving and cabinet and construction work.

Agba (*Gossweilerodendron balsamiferum*)
Nigeria. Gummy.

Balsa (*Ochroma spp*)
W. South America. Extremely light and soft. Used for model-making and insulation.

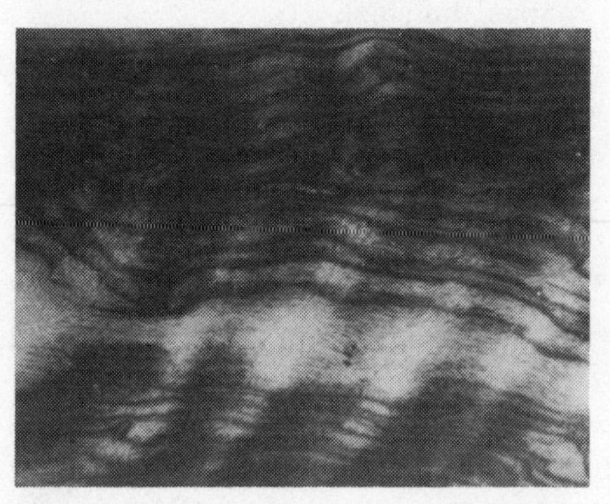

Fig. 127 *Ebony – showing its usual irregular black pigment – solid black is more rare.*

Ebony (*Dyospyros and Dalbergia* – various species.) Tropics. Very hard dense and dark, some types achieve full black.

Ekki (*Lophira procera*)
Nigeria. Extremely dense and strong. Constructional work.

Greenheart (*Ocotea rodiaei*)
S. America. Extremely dense and strong. Highly resistant and durable –

high alkaloid content. Construction work especially marine.

Hickory (*Carya and Hickoria spp*)
U.S.A. The most resilient material for impact tool handles.

Idigbo (*Terminalia ivorensis*)
W. Africa. Yellow brown. General purpose joinery or construction.

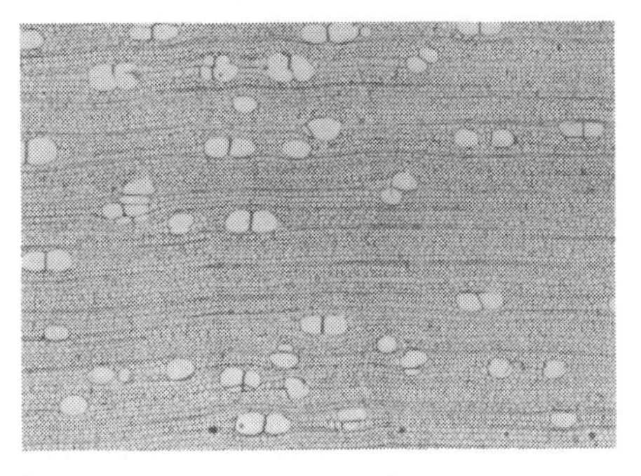

Fig. 128 *Jelutong cross section.*

Jelutong (*Dyera spp*)
Malaya. Light softish pale wood. Even textured. Works and finishes well. A good first hardwood for beginners.

Lignum vitae (*Guaiacum spp*)
C. America. The hardest and densest timber generally available. Small sizes. Very fine for turning – mallet heads. Very waxy – usable for wooden bearing surfaces e.g. plane soles.

Makore (*Dumoria heckelii*) and **Mansonia** (*Mansonia altissima*)
W. African. Fine cabinet timbers. Both dangerous due to irritant dust.

Obeche (*Triplochiton scleroxylon*)
Pale very soft with grain apparently resembling mahogany. Has been called White mahogany. General purposes and ply. Particularly good as pinboard – artists cutting board and dissecting board.

Padauk (*Pterocarpus dalbergioides*)
E. Indies. Scarlet – crimson

Pau Rosa (*Peltogyne densiflora*)
Brazil. Crimson – purple.

Purpleheart (*Peltogyne spp*)
Guyana. Purple. Used for fancy goods due to spectacular colours but small sizes available in Britain. All very fine strong construction timbers.

Ramin (*Gonystylus spp*)
Sarawak. Pale timber used for decorative mouldings due to its ease of staining almost any colour. Now rare. Has been overcropped.

Rosewood (Mostly *Dalbergia spp D. latifolia* – Indian rosewood)
Various tropical genera. Dense and dark. The best are much prized for instrument making, particularly pianos (often in veneer) and guitars.

Satinwood E. African (*Zanthoxylum spp* among others).
Highly decorative veneer. Satinwood is a widely used term for some very diverse tropical timbers of strange figuring.

Virola (*Virola koschnyi*)
C. America. Occasionally as drawer bottoms and sides. Not seen much in Britain.

Zebrano (*Brachystegia sp*)
W. Africa. Straw colour with spectacular black stripes. Often used for fancy articles and turning. Also available in cabinetmakers sizes. Works and finishes very well.

INDEX